Presented by
Kingston Minerals Limited
to commemorate the opening of
The Redeveloped Quarry and New Railhead
at
Penmaenmawr, Gwynedd
by
Wyn Roberts Esq MP
Parliamentary Under-Secretary of State
The Welsh Office

October 16th 1984

Out of the Rock . . .

Norman Bezzant

Out of the Rock...

With an Introduction by
Sir James Richards

HEINEMANN: LONDON

William Heinemann Ltd
10 Upper Grosvenor Street, London W1X 9PA

LONDON   MELBOURNE   TORONTO
JOHANNESBURG   AUCKLAND

First Published 1980

434 06900 0

*This is the first of two volumes, published in association
with The Bath and Portland Group.*

Text set in 11/13 pt Linotron 202 Bembo, printed and bound
in Great Britain at The Pitman Press, Bath

Contents

———— ✦ ————

Contents

Illustrations

Plates 33–40, between pages 180–181

13th Century Lacock Abbey: the Cloisters.
Longleat House.
Stone wharf at Corsham Station, circa 1905.
Stacking ground at Spring Quarry, Corsham.
Scappling stone blocks by hand and saw.
Spring Quarry, Corsham.
Mining methods at Hartham Park, Corsham.
Hand sawing at Monks Park.
Cutting out the bottom with an arc shearer.
A crane designed by John Lister-Kaye at Monks Park.
Winching up stone by electric motor from the Monks Park mine.
Original steam tractors drawing trailer-loads of stone.
A general view of Bottomcombe masonry works, 1931.

Plates 41–48, between pages 212–213

Processing stone at Bottomcombe: putting in a groove and drilling dowel-holes.
Bottomcombe: twin-bladed secondary saw and jointing off after planing.
West Wells Masonry Works.
Broadcasting House.
Cunard House.
Menin Gate.
Tyne Cot Cemetery at Passchendaele.
Panels with names of the missing dead at Thiepval.
The memorial at Thiepval.
Punching and tooling the shaft of a Cross of Remembrance.
The endless task of maintenance in War Cemeteries.
Experiments in painting-in the names of the missing dead on the Menin Gate.
Opencast coal operations west of Barnsley during the Second World War.

Acknowledgement is made to the following for permission to reproduce photographs: Mandy Reynolds, Fotique, Bath, Plates 1, 4(above) and 21(below); County Library, Bath, Plates 2, 4(below),

21(above) 22, 23, 24, and 25; National Monuments Records Office, Plates 3, 10, 11(below), 18(below), 33 and 34; Wells Cathedral archives (photographs by G. H. Hall, Taunton), Plates 6, 7(below) and 9; Somerset Public Records Office (photographs by Chapman & Son, Dawlish), Plates 7(above) and 8; Herbert, Weymouth, Plates 11(above) and 30; *Times* Newspaper, Plate 12; Edwin Smith, Plates 13(a), (c) and 14(above); Topical Press, Plate 13(b); Sims (Photographers), Plate 14(below); Keith Ellis, Plate 15; Fox Photos, Plate 16(above); Aerofilms and Aero Pictorial Ltd, Plate 16(below); Guildhall Library, London, Plates 17 and 19; A. F. Kersting, Plate 18(above); Conway Photo Library and Canon M. H. Ridgway, Plate 20; Bristol and West Photography, Plate 26; A. E. Mc. R. Pearce, Plate 32; Sport and General Agency, Plate 38(above); Marcus, Weymouth, Plate 40(below); Evan Jones, S. Dorset, Plate 41(below), 42(above) and 43(a); Sir Bannister Fletcher Library, (RIBA), Plate 44; Commonwealth War Graves Commission, Plates 45, 46, 47(b) and (c); A. J. Roberts, Barnsley, Plate 48(above).

Acknowledgement is also made to the following for permission to reproduce figures: Kingsmead Reprints, Bath, App. 1 Fig. 5; and the Curator, Holburne of Menstrie Museum, Bath, endpaper.

Acknowledgements

The author and publishers are grateful to the Chairman, Directors and staff of The Bath and Portland Group Limited and subsidiary companies for general assistance and advice. They also wish to acknowledge help given by the following: F. G. Dimes and Martyn Owen of the Institute of Geological Sciences, South Kensington; Stephen Green, Assistant Keeper of Archaeology, National Museum of Wales, Cardiff; J. H. Bettey MA, University of Bristol, and the Court Leet of the Island and Royal Manor of Portland; S. Ayles Crown Agent and Bailiff of the Royal Manor of Portland; the Very Rev. Dean Patrick Mitchell and the Chapter of Wells Cathedral; L. S. Colchester, historian to Wells Cathedral; B. Wheeler and J. R. Bambridge, successively Clerks of the Works at Wells Cathedral; The Worshipful Company of Masons, London; R. Crayford, at the Chapter House, St Paul's Cathedral; W. H. Dukes OBE, Director of Works, G. A. Cheater, Director of Information Services, and staff of the Commonwealth War Graves Commission, Maidenhead; R. F. Pickford, Curatorial Assistant, Geology, and G. M. Huggins, County Library, Bath; R. J. Tucker, founder of the Free Troglophile Association, Bristol; A. Tonge, Clerk of the Council, Fortuneswell, Portland; County Library, Queen Square, Bath; Local History Library (Somerset County Library) Taunton; Somerset Public Records Office, Taunton;

Acknowledgements

Conwy County Library, Gwynedd; Gwynedd Public Records Office; Guildhall Library, London; Public Records Office, London; National Monuments Record Office, London; Sir Bannister Fletcher Library (RIBA), London; Suffolk County Library, Bury St Edmunds; The Roman Baths, Bath; Portland Museum, Easton; North Wales Quarrying Museum, Gwynedd; and Canal Museum, Llangollen.

Introduction
By Sir James Richards

IT IS ALMOST true to say that the history of English architecture is the history of building in stone. There are of course other materials, notably timber and brick; but timber survives through the centuries only when protected from the weather, and brick, which was introduced by the Romans and fell into disuse when they left, was rediscovered in the thirteenth century and employed thereafter richly and variously, though most often domestically. Neither can compete with stone as the material of great architecture. Stone has been synonymous with fine building since the Saxon disciples of St. Augustine used it to give dignity and permanence to their new Christian churches, to the time when, for technical and economic reasons, steel and concrete structures were preferred to those based on load-bearing materials yet nevertheless continued to present stone facings and facades to the eye.

By building stone we usually mean limestone. We must not overlook some useful sandstones nor the dense but difficult-to-work granites that occur all round the fringes of these islands from eastern Scotland west and south to Cornwall; but it is the continuous band of limestone running diagonally across England from Dorset to Yorkshire that constitutes the most valuable source of building stone. Its quality and power of endurance can be seen at a glance by anyone who travels over this part of England, where the skyline is constantly enriched by the towers of parish churches more splendid than those elsewhere and the valleys ennobled by stone-built villages and towns.

This exceptionally fine limestone emerges most abundantly in the south-west, on the island of Portland in Dorset, at Ham Hill and Doulting in Somerset, and around Bath. It has the advantage

1

of acquiring a beautiful range of subtle colours when washed by English weather and of withstanding the polluted atmosphere of cities—which cannot be said of all limestones: witness the notorious delapidation of the Houses of Parliament, for which a magnesian limestone from the Anston quarries in the West Riding of Yorkshire was unwisely chosen. The silvery patina typical of London's major monuments we owe first to Inigo Jones but especially to Sir Christopher Wren, who imported stone from the Portland quarries in enormous quantities for St. Paul's and the City churches and was scientist enough to understand the value of careful selection and skilful quarrying.

Before their day London was only to a limited extent a city built with stone, having none available close by. Small quantities of the modest Kentish rag (itself a kind of limestone) were brought from not far away, and for some important buildings a beautiful stone had come by sea from Normandy. But London was transformed into a city with its noblest buildings all of stone when the wonderful West Country oolitic limestone was brought all the way from the Isle of Portland to the capital. This was strong and hard but capable of being finely carved, thus lending itself to the precision and control demanded by the newly introduced Renaissance style of architecture.

Stone from the Portland quarries and from those in the region round Bath travelled—in increasing quantities as transport improved—to many places besides London, with the result that almost the whole range of English architectural styles could be illustrated by buildings made of stone from these quarries. This book however embraces a great deal more than architecture. Buildings and their construction naturally run through it as a central theme because they are the main purpose to which the stone was—and still is—put, especially the stone produced by the now combined Bath and Portland companies who have sponsored its publication. But the special interest of *Out of the Rock . . .* is that it puts both the quarrying and the architectural employment of the stone into their social context.

In this it is in my experience unique. I can enumerate here only a few of the aspects of English life and history touched on in a book that is the more lively and evocative for leaping from one unexpected subject to another rather than providing a strictly chronological narrative. The Industrial Revolution naturally plays a prominent part, and especially the construction of the canal system that opened up the market for building stone. So do the relations between masters and men, the technology and the progressive mechanization of stone-getting and the business of quarry owning, together with the families it brought into prominence; also the nineteenth-century improvement in road-making that allowed the best building-stone, as noted above, to be carried where it was most wanted, material from the limestone quarries being itself a principal contributor to harder and smoother roads and remaining so to a great extent even after McAdam had replaced it by crushed igneous rock for his new road-making system.

More surprising topics are touched on also, but all relevant to the book's purpose; the use of underground galleries in the stone quarries at Corsham, for example, for storing munitions in the First World War and the use of quarries for safeguarding art-treasures in the Second. But how is it, the reader must discover for himself, that besides perhaps predictable (but none-the-less fascinating) accounts of the making of neolithic stone axes, of the setting-out methods of medieval masons and the use of horse-power in stone-quarries as late as 1950, the author includes descriptions of the formation of the War Graves Commission and of the key role played (again in the Second World War) by The Bath and Portland Stone firms in perfecting the Asdic instrument used for detecting submarines.

This book can be enjoyed not only as a specialized segment of industrial history but as a series of side-lights thrown on the social history of England, made all the more illuminating by the unusual angle from which they are examined.

1

A Piece of Infinity

DURING THE CLOSING years of the nineteenth century a number of west country quarrymen united to avoid trading against each other and hence to broaden their sphere of activities. In this they succeeded, and went on to draw together most of the companies quarrying and carving stone from the precious chain of Jurassic limestones that separates the hard igneous rocks of north and west England from the soft sedimentary deposits of the east and south. Their interests, which had centred on Bath, were first extended to Portland and then progressively to old quarries at Ham, Doulting, Beer, Guiting, and Clipsham—each name associated with a distinctive quality of building stone.

Two world wars came and went and the quarrymen, spurred on by progress in kindred industries and the discovery of new forms of power, next turned to igneous rock, which in the twentieth century has been increasingly essential to road and rail development. Quarries at Penmaenmawr and Trevor in North Wales, Tonfanau and Llansawel in Central Wales, and at Gwalchmai in Anglesey were brought into the Group, and further mineral activities were to follow. So far the interests had been restricted to stone in a variety of forms, yet after the Second World War the Group interests were becoming complex, and the latitude and liberty offered by diversification was calling.

To appreciate fully how the quarrymen had arrived at this juncture, it is necessary to understand, at the onset of this book, something of the character and qualities of the material that absorbed their energies and developed their skills. Stone was not

4

created to their order: true, it was there for the taking, but it had been forming through millions of years, and the characteristics that fitted various stones for varying purposes were to reveal many of the secrets of creation.

In this volume, the story of stone and its fashioning into materials for man's needs has been told from the world's formation up to the middle 1940's. As the chapter titles indicate, it is a story that brings together many seemingly disparate segments and which combines social, religious, and political history with geology and ecology; it tells of cause and effect as Iberians, Celts, Romans, Saxons, and Normans invaded Britain; of church and monarch as patrons of masonry and stone building; of the Industrial Revolution and the essential part played by stone in its development.

Through all the ages the processes of evolution are demonstrated chronologically by reference to quarries, mines, and masonry works that have now come into the control of The Bath and Portland Group. Their history is in part the history of England. It is a history that starts quite literally at the beginning.

Man is ill-equipped to contemplate the infinite. The ultimate distance beyond a star and the beginning of time have defeated the philosophers, and meanwhile lesser mortals must be content with religious allegory to interpret the mysteries of creation. It is not surprising that primitive man, the unique possessor of imagination, developed many theories to account for his being and for the world about him. Legends of lost worlds—such as Lemuria, Atlantis, Osiris, and Rama were handed down from generation to generation; stories survived of the continents of Mu and Poseid disappearing into the oceans at times of cataclysm—violent disturbances in the earth's crust.

But what prehistoric man did not realise was that many of the secrets of creation lay in stone, the very material to which he had first turned for strength and comfort. And if he failed to realise this, so too did his successors, right down to the seventeenth and eighteenth centuries *anno domini*. It was Steno, a Dane living in Italy around 1650 who, from a study of rocks of differing origin, first concluded that fossils in stone must represent the remains of early organic life. The development of geology as a science took its time however, and a hundred years passed before Werner,

5

professor of mineralogy at Freiberg, classified the rocks of the Harz mountains, grouping them in a definite succession corresponding to the events of history. He established an influential mining school, but was discredited for his theory that all rocks were precipitated in a constant succession from a common chaotic fluid, formed under water; this theory earned for him and his followers the title 'neptunists' while his critics were termed 'vulcanists'.

More sensible were the views of James Hutton of Edinburgh, who at the close of the eighteenth century developed a 'Theory of the Earth'. Hutton was veering towards later proofs when he observed the nature of current changes in the earth's crust, which he claimed were similar to changes that had taken place in the distant past. Though scepticism persisted for some fifty years, Hutton's theories were promulgated by John Playfair, at a time when the alternate 'Catastrophic Theory' of Cuvier, a Frenchman, was in vogue. The catastrophists sought to explain the succession of rocks as resulting from times of earthquake, flood and volcanic action of far greater intensity than those currently experienced. By their theory, animal life was killed off at these times, to be replaced by new.

It remained for William Smith, a West Country surveyor who was working on the canal system in Somerset, to digest all these theories and relate them to the practical knowledge of stone which he had gained through his occupation. William Smith could be described as the first working geologist, for geology had previously been the hobby of the leisured rich. Smith was in a position to appreciate the economic importance of this new science in the rise of industry. He had seen fossils in the rocks of the canal bed, and by characterizing the fossils in different stones, he developed a classification which could be correlated with rocks of other areas. Smith went on to draw up with remarkable accuracy the first geological maps of Britain. Despite his considerable contribution, Smith always remained a believer in the Catastrophic Theory.

But it was Charles Lyell, by his philosophical writings in the early 1830's, who presented the first balanced and reasoned review of geology as a whole. He supported Hutton's writings and denounced the Catastrophic Theory. Lyell's viewpoint was 'uniformitarian'—denying the occurrence of cataclysms greater than those of the present day: modern research certainly shows that the major changes in the world's crust have developed slowly over millions of years. Of more importance was Lyell's acceptance of sedimentary as well as volcanic origin of rock, and of the agents working to affect the earth's crust today. The secrets that had been locked in stone through millions of years were starting to break out.

Just as space measurement in 'light-years' is implicit in astrology, so the expression 'geological time' has evolved in relation to the eternal development of rock systems. Geological time, measured in thousands of millions of years, is always approximate, for geology is a science of progressive knowledge which will always remain a combination of theory and proof. However, methods of detection are constantly improving, and the loose geological concepts of two hundred years ago have already found close links with related sciences, and have led to the development of new sciences specializing in branches of geology. Thus today we have physical, structural, historical, and applied branches of geology, each making its own contribution to twentieth century civilization, and each finding common ground with other sciences.

Physical geology deals with the natural agencies which produce changes in the world's surface. From what may be observed to be happening to the earth's crust today comes an understanding of the processes of the past. The physical agencies are grouped as internal or external. The internal changes are brought about most dramatically by volcanic action, producing lava and other hot materials, or by sudden movements such as earthquakes under the earth's surface. Less dramatic are the slow rise and fall of land levels, evident in the existence of submerged forests and raised beaches. The study of the rocks of Britain shows clearly that during most of prehistory, the drifting mass that was to become Britain was submerged, though it emerged several times to submerge again.

Most of the external changes have at their root the influence of the atmosphere. Wind, rain, and temperature changes (responsible for subaerial denudation) all have an effect on the surface of rocks and very slowly cause their disintegration, and the particles of rock so broken down form a covering of soil. Usually the deposit created relates in composition to the rock beneath it, but hills, rivers, and rain cause movement of the soil to lower levels. Rainwater serves several purposes; apart from being taken up by plant life, it may evaporate, form surface water, or percolate through the soil and through rock fissures to form 'ground water' at lower levels. Ground water may attack and dissolve part of the stone it encounters, and this is noticeable in limestone country where it can hollow out caves, leave salt deposits, and surface again in the form of springs.

The eroding effect of rivers is usually, though not always, responsible for the formation of the valleys, gorges and canyons through which they flow. The alluvium thus removed from high ground may be deposited in marshland and deltas, or carried straight out into the sea. Finally, the sea itself is responsible for external change in the erosion of coastal land and in the movement of soil through fast-moving currents. This marine denudation is counterbalanced to some extent by the new sedimentary deposits that it builds up in other places.

Here we have been talking about normal activity in normal times. But through volcanic action and earth movements, new mineral deposits have slowly formed throughout the world from mountain top to ocean bed. The proof of these changes lies in the stratigraphic pattern of the earth's crust. Sedimentary rocks, and volcanic lava associated with them, are found in layers (beds or strata) which are frequently quite flat and regular; the layers represent successive deposits, and almost always the lower layers, as one would expect, are older than the upper. Starting as horizontal layers, these deposits have often been disturbed, and tend to 'dip'; where this occurs, rocks of different strata will rise to the surface at an angle and crop out at different places. It does not follow that rock at the earth's surface is the youngest, for many of those cropping out for instance in Wales and Scotland, are older than some rocks of southern England lying a thousand metres or more below-ground.

Stratified rocks have done more than 'dip', however. Deeper movements of the earth's crust have often squeezed the stratified rock into folds. Rock that has failed to 'fold' under such pressures tends to break up, producing the faults in the earth's crust which, through their weakness, are often the scene of earthquakes. Another feature of sedimentary rock is the intrusion of molten lava into it, either along the beds formed by varying deposits, or cutting right through the rock grain. Such lava eventually cools and forms slowly into igneous rock, called 'sills' when in the plane of the beds, or 'dykes' when cutting across them, the former being concordant and the latter discordant intrusions. Within the sedimentary rock itself are joint planes which are of great significance in quarrying, for not only do they determine the size and shape of the blocks that are quarried but they also determine the strength of the roof in stone mining operations.

For three hundred and fifty years, man has been probing the origin of the continents and oceans we know today. Originally, hypotheses were based on observation and coincidence: Sir Francis Bacon in 1620 suggested that the similarity of the coastlines of Africa and South America (which can be likened to complementary pieces of a jigsaw puzzle) could hardly be accidental, and the theory, first known as the Drifting of Continents slowly developed. By the mid-nineteenth century, geological as well as geographical phenomena were observed: the fitting together of Africa and America explained the existence of the same fossils in coal deposits on each side of the Atlantic. In the first quarter of the twentieth century the facts were emerging; most of the discussion concerned the work, published in 1915 and 1924, of the German astronomer Alfred Wegener, who has subsequently been acknowledged as the pioneer of the theory of continental drift.

Up to this time, geologists had concentrated on the evidence of the continents themselves, ignoring the oceans, covering two-thirds of the Earth's surface, that lay between them. It was not until the late 1950's that a mid-ocean mountain ridge three kilometres in height and hundreds of kilometres wide was discovered, running between the world's continents, and extending in all to some 80,000 kilometres in length. A small part of this ridge runs down the mid-Atlantic from Iceland via the Azores to Tristan da Cunha. The mid-ocean ridge is composed of volcanic rock and the ocean bed stretching away to each side is covered by sediments one kilometre in depth. Along the summit of this Atlantic ridge a rift valley is slowly dividing the mountains. The valley is already about 2000 metres deep and 50 kilometres wide; it is spreading at the rate of one centimetre a year in each direction.

British and American oceanographic expeditions in the late 1950's found that the ridge extends not only from the Atlantic round Africa and through the Indian Ocean to the Gulf, but also between Australia and Antarctica, and finally linking with a ridge valley running northwards through the eastern Pacific. The ridge is broken again and again by tremendous fractures in the Earth's surface. From these and other studies the picture of the Earth's shell now emerging shows that it is composed of seven primary 'plates'—vast slabs of Earth some 80 to 100 kilometres in depth which are moving separately over a soft under-mantle. It is at the boundaries of these plates that the worlds' earthquakes and volcanoes are concentrated. Here the plates may collide, divide, or glide past one another; the most dramatic activity is centred in the collision zones, such as in the San Andreas Fault system down the Pacific Coast of North America. This is where the North American and Pacific plates are moving together at the rate of five centimetres a year; this was the cause of the great earthquake of San Francisco in 1906. The Eurasian, African, Indo-Australian, China and South America plates cover the rest of the world's surface, excluding the polar regions.

This fast-developing science of the structure of the world's rocks, the manner of their arrangement, and the effect of time in altering their character, is called plate tectonics. Current research will undoubtedly reveal the processes and history by which the ancient super-continent of Pangaea gradually broke up to form the continents we know today. Already tectonics has probed and identified the stupendous forces within the Earth's interior which cause these movements, and has attributed the formation of primary ores to the heat generated by plate movements, affecting crustal rocks.

Tectonic studies have brought recognition for a third rock classification: metamorphic rock. This is the name attributed to pre-existing rock which, through subsequent pressures and heat, has changed its character dramatically. It is now held by some experts that certain so-called igneous rocks have changed from original sedimentary rock by extreme metamorphic pressures. Among those so classified are slates which originated as clays and shale; marbles evolving from limestones; and rocks, such as gneiss and schist, having many different origins.

The branch of the science of geology which deals with the origin of the rocks of the earth's crust is petrology, and the petrologic cycle, by definition, explains in a few words the eternal processes of rock change. The cycle of change starts with the weathering of surface rocks giving deposits which eventually form sedimentary rocks. Thrust down into deeper levels by collision of the plates the sedimentary rocks may melt to give magma which subsequently cools to produce granitic rock. The rock thus formed cools, and if exposed on the earth's surface, can in turn weather to form sedimentary rock, and so the cycle continues.

Petrologists not only observe what is visible to the naked eye in the relationship of rock masses, but their work with the microscope has contributed richly to the value of their science. Thin sections of rock, no more than three-hundredths of a millimetre thick, may be examined on glass slips under the petrological microscope; the constituent minerals can then be identified from their optical qualities, and their textures, constituent proportions, and mutual arrangement, established. All this interpretative work contributes markedly to knowledge of world history. Petrologists also research through mechanical analysis, in which stone is broken down into individual mineral grains for grading, usually by sieving or elutriation (separating in a stream of air or water). This mechanical analysis is invaluable to industries using stone in the form of blocks, facings, and aggregates. Laboratory work, in physiochemical experiments to produce evidence of behavioural analogies, completes the range of methods whereby petrology has converted rock, metaphorically, into 'documents of ancient yet measurable age'. Indeed by the study of radio-active uranium and thorium isotopes, it has now been established with reasonable certainty that the date when lead isotopes (produced in the constant disintegration of these elements) first began to accumulate in the earth's crust, was over 5000 million years ago, which can approximate to the age of the world itself.

The earliest system, the Pre-cambrian, occupies approximately 4000 million years of geological time. There followed the Palaeozoic system of about 340 million years duration. The Lower

Palaeozoic rocks (Cambrian, Ordovician and Silurian) were mostly formed under the sea. The Upper Palaeozoic group, which includes the Devonian, found over much of Britain, was also formed under the sea, except for the Old Red Sandstone which was of terrestial origin. The Carboniferous rocks, above the Devonian, are characterized by the many coal seams mined in Britain; and the desert Permian rocks, named from the Russian province of Perm, lie above the Carboniferous. The Mesozoic rocks were formed during the next 170 million years. The lowest strata are triassic; then comes the Jurassic (named for the Jura Mountains) which is characterized by clays, muddy limestones and the famous oolitic limestones. The uppermost part of the Mesozoic system is the cretaceous layer, at the top of which is the layer of limestone known as the Chalk (very pure limestone).

Tertiary or Cainozoic strata of sedimentary rocks were deposited over a period generally taken at 65 million years; the earliest (Eocene) system is represented in the sands and clays of the London and Hampshire basins and in volcanic basalts, and the later Oligocene system by volcanic intrusions in the Islands of Skye, Mull, and Arran. The later Pliocene rocks are evident in East Anglia. The comparatively short Quaternary period includes the Pleistocene Ice Age rocks which may be seen over nearly all of Britain; and we now live in the milder Holocene epoch, the last 10,000 years of the geologist's time-scale.

It was during the Pleistocene that man emerged as *homo sapiens.* For research into the origins of life, the observations of Steno and William Smith were pursued, and the science of palaeontology has resulted—the study of fossils and extinct organisms. Life on earth started with invertebrates of different kinds, long before any evidence points to the existence of vertebrates. It has been established that through the more recent phases of geological time, forms of vertebrate life on the earth's surface have evolved continuously, developing from the forms that preceded them; this means that no forms of life were cut off and lost for ever in cataclysms or similar catastrophies, at least according to current experience and opinion. Since these conclusions are based largely on fossils occurring in rocks it is logical to measure the evolution of animal life by the later series of rock systems—those in which these various fossils were found.

First there came, at the end of the Pre-Cambrian epoch, and during the Silurian and Devonian epochs which followed, the Age of Fishes. Early fish-like creatures had no jaws or paired fins, but these slowly evolved to the point where the fins were modified into legs and the Age of Amphibia followed. Characteristically, Amphibians are primarily aquatic, in later life breathing air, developing legs, and walking on land. As the Permian epoch approached, the amphibia started to show the true structural features of reptiles and during the Age of Reptiles which then began, an amazing series of metamorphoses occurred. Reptiles existed in sizes ranging from that of a mouse to that dwarfing the elephant; reptiles became biped as well as quadruped; and, as pterodactyls, developed an apparatus which enabled them to glide from high to low land. The subsequent development of feathers produced true birds during the Cretaceous epoch.

In Triassic and Jurassic times early examples of the mammal were evolving, and the Age of Mammals commenced with the Tertiary epoch of rock formation. At this time the mammals advanced and the reptiles declined. Fish ruled the sea, birds ruled the air, and it was as though reptiles had only been created in advanced form as a catalyst to enable mammals to go forward into the quaternary epoch, with man as the supreme specie. Palaeontology and stratigraphy will thus be seen to be complementary. The palaeontologist constructs the history of life from fossils, while the stratigrapher divines the timescale of later stones from that history.

All the aspects of geology that have been considered here combine to serve another even greater purpose in the modern economy. Applied geology is today an economic necessity, for it provides essential information on the subterranean distribution of all minerals. Silica alone accounts for 60% of the earth's crust: alumina, 15%: and iron oxides 7%. Five other oxides bring the identified proportion up to 96%, while the principal metallic ores account for part only of the remaining fraction. Industry thus relies heavily on the geologist for the facts about these materials. The distribution of coalfields and mineral ores in mining areas, the migration of oil and water along pervious beds and the difficulties of locating them, are a few of the problems requiring an intimate knowledge of rock structure. Geology is equally critical in the engineering and construction industries where soil infrastructure and drift deposits virtually control the design and method of constructing major projects such as reservoirs, dams, bridges, highways and heavy industrial buildings.

Something has been said of the beginnings of geology as a recognised science. It is perhaps strange that the British, whose country occupies only a minute part of the world's surface, were responsible for most of the pioneer work which resulted in the science of geology and its proliferation into many parts; even stranger that within this small land every major formation of the geological succession occurs, with only one exception, the Miocene. The British stratigraphical succession has become virtually a world standard.

The geological foundation and topography of Britain are not unnaturally interlinked. The mountainous part of Britain lies west and north of a line drawn roughly from Torquay to Hartlepool (but keeping to the east of the Pennines), and in this part the older rocks of the Pre-Cambrian and Palaeozoic epochs are found at the surface, with the valuable ores and minerals occurring beneath. Among the major varieties of these stones of the north and west are the older igneous and metamorphic rocks, which have provided Britain with most of her primary road-making materials; slate in the Cambrian, Ordovician and Silurian; and coal in the Carboniferous masses.

East and south of the Torquay/Hartlepool line, the younger Mesozoic and Tertiary rocks lie on the surface. Here ores and minerals occur less frequently. At least two-thirds of this area is covered with rocks of the Cretaceous age, with the Chalk predominating. In it there occurs the belt of great Oolitic limestones taken from the rocks of the Jurassic system, running north-north-east from Portland to Whitby, which has provided southern England with much of her building stone.

When the geologist describes Jurassic limestone as one of the younger rocks, he is not forgetting that it is perhaps more than 140 million years old, but he is comparing it with Pre-Cambrian rocks some of which are several thousand million years old. It is difficult to contemplate such a length of time, and even that was not the beginning. If we remember that European man was a barbarian only 4000 years ago and that civilisation as we know it has developed since that time—a mere 250th part of one million years—we can start to appreciate what a microscopic piece of infinity we occupy. Even smaller is the period of scientific discovery set in motion by the Industrial Revolution; and this is the period that mostly concerns our story.

2

Stone Age Man

THE PARTNERSHIP OF man and stone goes back into pre-history. The Stone Age is defined as the stage in which man was ignorant of metals and relied upon stone implements and softer materials shaped by their use; it has been sub-divided into three periods: the Old Stone Age (palaeolithic), the Middle Stone Age (mesolithic), and the New Stone Age (neolithic). These periods all fall within the comparatively short Quaternary epoch of rock formation by which time *homo sapiens* had evolved in his modern form. Relics of the Old Stone Age from south-east Europe include hand-axes or 'bifaces', made by reducing nodules to a desired shape, and there is also evidence of the use of a variety of primitive implements including animal bones, bows and arrows, spears, and even a pronged salmon spear.

Evidence of the occupation of Portland Island during the Old and Middle Stone Ages has been established, and it is interesting that among many stone implements found near Portland Bill, there were 'fire-reddened stones', a grim reminder of the proximity of Portland to the great ice cap. For during the Old Stone Age the British Isles were ice-bound north of the line of the Kennet and Thames rivers. A few intrepid men ventured into the Peak District during the Old Stone Age, but only as the ice receded was northern Britain truly habitable; and so man moved north from southern England and from Europe—especially from Iberia. He was no longer a savage, but a barbarian with a knowledge of stone which he already knew how to cut and polish.

The New Stone Age is reckoned to have dated from the third

millenium BC in northern Europe, though in south-east Europe it may have dated from the sixth millenium BC. The perilous ledges and hill caves of Britain gave the insurgent neolithic man protection from animal, enemy, and element, and he soon discovered the scree with which he would continue lithic industries to meet his basic needs of food, warmth, and comfort. Polished hand-axes and adzes were the fundamental requirement, for by their use wood could be cut and shaped, producing bows, arrows and spearshafts for the hunt; materials for improving primitive living quarters; and fuel for firing. The polished 'celt', an early cutting and cleaving instrument, enabled man to convert forest into farming land, and he set about the task of developing a farm industry.

Hand-axe, spearhead, knife, pick, adze and chisel are all evident among the range of relics brought together in British archeological surveys, and it is notable that by the neolithic period man had already appraised stone hardnesses and discovered the most durable rocks for his purposes. The sites of three main axe factories have been identified, at Penmaenmawr and Myndd Rhiw in Clwyd, and at Langdale Pikes, west of Grasmere in Cumbria; geological evidence suggests that axe factories also existed in the Pembroke hills running down to Ramsey Island. Petrologically each stone is distinctive, and by examination in thin section its place of origin can be identified with certainty, no matter how far it has travelled.

Penmaenmawr, 'the Head of the Great Rock', is about 1500 feet high, and stands on the coast at the northern extremity of the Snowdon range. Although its axe factory was the most recent discovery, the mountain is rich in other antiquities of later origin. A druid's circle standing on the mountain's eastern shoulder was earlier described by R. Mortimer Wheeler as the best surviving stone circle in Wales, while at the summit a number of hut circles had been discovered within the area of an early iron-age hill-fort; and relics of a number of graves, as monoliths and tumuli, were found high on the moors behind the mountain.

At Penmaenmawr the pale-grey rock used by primitive man for axe-making originated as intrusions of one large and two small igneous masses of silurian age into the earlier (ordovician) shales of the area. The ordovician and silurian systems are named for the

Ordovices and Silures, tribes of Britons who at different times inhabited the areas of this rock system. Microscopically, the Penmaenmawr rock consists of small crystals of feldspar, augite and pyroxene distributed in a micro-crystalline matrix of quartz, felspar and magnetite. This fine-textured rock is described as an 'augite-granophyre'.

The site above Penmaenmawr is known among geologists as the 'Graig Lwyd Group of Factories', because of the existence of the main mass on Graig Lwyd itself, supplemented by the two smaller masses, Dinas and Garreg Fawr, standing off at about a mile inland at the same altitude. Though all the stone is consistent in hardness and durability, the desirable property of easy flaking is noticeable at the margins of the main mass, and particularly at the outlying masses of Dinas and Garreg Fawr. This is due to the more rapid original cooling of the mass at the fringes, giving a more finely crystalline texture to the rock. For this reason the main flaking areas were at Dinas and Garreg Fawr.

The discovery of the factory in 1919 was made after the fashion of a paper chase, by following a trail of 'human flakes'. A Graig Lwyd axe had been discovered in 1890, but its full significance had not then been appreciated. Also Col. C. H. Darbishire, who with his family had taken over the Graig Lwyd quarries in 1878, had discovered prehistoric burial mounds on the hills above the quarries, and had also come across a few 'roughouts', as the unfinished axes are called.

It was not until G. Hazzledine Warren arrived with his wife for a holiday at Penmaenmawr in 1919 that serious thought was given to the possible existence of an ancient monument. When walking on the Green Gorge above the quarries, Warren recognized the 'human flakes' which man had made using hammer stones— waterworn cobblestones taken from stream beds and from the foreshore. The position of many of the flakes gave some clue to the centres of earlier activity; many were found along a path up the mountainside cut by German prisoners during the Great War. Warren's wife in her rambles also happened upon several rough-outs and even one or two axes. The excited Warren returned to London and lectured on his find to the Royal Anthropological Institute, at the same time appealing for funds to excavate the site; the contributions came mostly from universities and museums.

Warren returned in 1920, and with a gang of eight or nine men, set to work, receiving fine measure of co-operation from Col. Darbishire. The quarry provided tools, equipment, and much-needed advice, and Ivor E. Davies, then managing the quarry stores, acted as liaison between the quarry and the exploring party, and as a general factotum to Warren himself.

By the process of denudation through the centuries, the axe factory sites had disappeared below an accumulation of black peaty soil, on which ling and heather now flourished, making research more difficult. Over a period of two years, excavations were opened at about fifteen places on the scree below Graig Lwyd; most were close to the edge of the recently quarried area. Three revealed working floors, of which one proved to be the site of a large hearth some 20 feet in diameter, with a base 'formed of selected stones three to five inches in diameter, covered by a good deal of charcoal, and many axes and flakes, more or less burnt'. Round this hearth and a number of smaller hearths nearby were accumulations of small chips produced in the final trimming process. But apart from the tools of axe manufacture and some unpolished axes, the finds were restricted to four broken polished axes—three of them reflaked (possibly indicating a repair service)—and some waste flakes trimmed into scrapers and points. Two working floors were explored above the quarry, of which one had produced axes similar to those made below the quarry. Finally two stone-built hut-circles were excavated below the steepest crags of Graig Lwyd.

Warren went on to make a study of the technique of axe manufacture, and distinguished three stages in the production of the roughouts made at Graig Lwyd. First, selected scree was roughly flaked on an anvil stone or sometimes the roughouts may have consisted merely of thick flakes taken from large blocks of scree. A number of large beach pebbles and boulders, all battered, were found and identified as hammer stones; these were used in the intermediate stage to remove long flakes reaching beyond the centre line of the core. The final trimming was then devoted to producing a reasonably straight and regular edge, and an even surface. The first stage could be effectively bypassed by using tabular-formed rock having parallel joint-planes, sometimes little more than one inch apart. The method of flaking invariably produced roughouts with asymmetrical planes, so that, for instance, where one plane was almost flat—by accident or design—the implement became an adze. Similarly narrow roughouts could have been intended for chisels. Generally the final form of the implement would be governed by its intended use, though clearly a suitably shaped piece of scree would first be selected.

The finishing process, which significantly was not carried out at the axe-factory, consisted of grinding and polishing, primarily to produce a smooth and regular cutting edge; many of the implements, however, were polished over their whole surface. The edges of the roughouts were wavy, as might be expected from the flaking of their alternate surfaces during manufacture. It was therefore usual for the finishers to grind a narrow flat strip on each side. This grinding and polishing could have been done anywhere where abrasive material and water were available, and the known distribution of Graig Lwyd products suggests that the finishing was generally done in North Wales, as only two axes (so far discovered) have found their way out of Wales as roughouts.

The conclusions drawn by archaeologists suggest that the makers of axes were skilled to the degree of specialization by spending much of the year in pursuit of their craft. Although the large hearth at Graig Lwyd suggests work in winter conditions, no traces of permanent settlement have been discovered in the immediate vicinity; several small valleys nearby offered suitable shelter, however, and one above Llanfairfechan yielded small traces of habitation. Otherwise, the nearest traces of neolithic settlement are those found on the Great Orme's Head, and at Llandegai, a mile outside Bangor. It is possible that the axe-makers travelled seasonally from Wessex, which represented a considerable part of the market for finished axes: this has not been discounted. But though Mynydd Rhiw also has some minor traces of habitation, it is accepted that the mountain screes and crags of Wales would only serve for the basic production of roughouts; surrounding shelters would not yield the full range of spiritual, social, and subsistence activities necessary to indigenous existence.

It seems more probable, therefore, that the axe-makers came from Llandegai, the site of two of the formalized stone circles adopted by neolithic communities which gave the word 'henge' to

The Roman Bath with the south face of Bath Abbey in the background.

(Above) Gilded bronze head of Minerva unearthed in Stall Street, Bath, in 1727.
(Below) The original offices of The Bath Stone Firms Limited in Abbey Yard, photographed circa 1912.

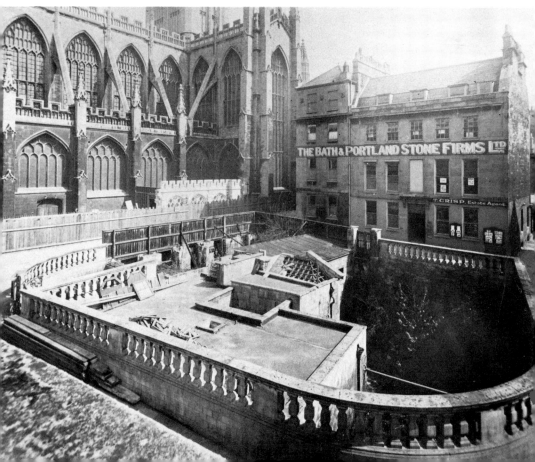

(Above) From Doulting quarry came stone for Glastonbury Abbey, rebuilt by St Dunstan and largely destroyed by fire in 1184.
(Below) The Church of St Lawrence, Bradford-on-Avon, probably the oldest Saxon church in England, thought to be built of stone from Hazelbury Quarry.

(Above) The floodlit west face of Bath Abbey, depicting Bishop King's dream of angels climbing ladders (1495).
(Below) Bath Abbey, masterpiece in the perpendicular style, showing the fan-vaulting of William Vertue.

(Above) Horses at Mallams on the Isle of Portland being used to brake the descent of stone to the quayside.

(Below) Block of Portland stone measured and marked at 42 cubic feet.

Wells Cathedral. The nave looking east: the inverted arches were erected in 1338 to support the dipping central tower.

(Above) Effigy of Jack Blandiver, Wells Cathedral. (Below) The west front of Wells Cathedral: the masonry and carvings are all in Doulting stone.

(Above) Vicars Close, or the College of Vicars at Wells; 14th and 15th Centuries. Perhaps 'the oldest street in England'.

(Below) Town and Cathedral are named for the Well of St Andrew.

archaeological terminology. The henge at Llandegai North has been dated about 2500 BC, and that at Llandegai South a few hundred years later, the latter a 'deliberately modernized replacement to serve a community directly in succession to the earlier one'. The dates of Llandegai coincide with those of the Graig Lwyd factory operation. Most significant was the discovery in the northern henge circle at Llandegai of a cremation burial accompanied by a roughed-out block of Pembroke stone 'polished to a glassy smoothness on its underside apparently by use for axe polishing, presumably the personal equipment of the individual so buried'. Also at Llandegai was found a pit containing Graig Lwyd axe fragments.

The marketing of neolithic axes was organized to a remarkable degree. Although the factories in Cumbria and Clwyd enjoyed their own local areas of distribution, they shared a common market in Wessex. There is no conclusive evidence of the means and method of distribution: it probably involved both hand-to-hand barter of single implements and 'deliberate trading journeys' where implements were carried in quantity. There is reason to favour coastal routes rather than overland routes for these journeys, as there were outlying centres of distribution at Bournemouth and possibly also in the Severn estuary. This theory is supported by the occurrence of a single Graig Lwyd axe at Land's End.

Since England north of a line running roughly between the Kennet and the Thames had been ice-bound prior to the Stone Age, the Wessex settlements would pre-date those farther north. As the ice slowly receded, it seems probable, therefore, that the men of Wessex would have gradually explored the west coast as far north as Cumbria, thus discovering indigenous material for the manufacture of axes, possibly replacing earlier axes of European origin. In this way the link between the western axe-factories and the distant Wessex market would appear logical.

Modern archaeology has dated the Great Langdale and Graig Lwyd factories at about 2750–2500 BC by radiocarbon attribution, and it is estimated that they may have flourished for a 1000 years, thereafter failing slowly in the face of first bronze and then iron competition. But the significance of the axe industry in inter-community contacts during the neolithic age is paramount.

The dealers in stone implements provided a means for the dissemination and exchange of ideas in socio-religious practices, such as are observed in the henge monument which eventually outmoded the causewayed enclosure, typified at Avebury. It is noticeable that the henge monument (Llandegai North was the earliest) was fundamentally a centre for religious and social purposes in neolithic settlements. The connotation of Druid sacrificial practices associated with Stonehenge dates only from the first century BC.

By the advent of the Romans in Britain, neolithic man had become an experienced farmer, producing crops and rearing stock which assured his own food supply and enabled larger communities to develop. Underground caves on Portland, which have been named the 'Portland Beehives', were used for the storage of grain in the Iron Age; possibly this was a new use for what had originally been cave dwellings, for by this time man was capable of building surface homes of wattle and mud to his own design. The canoe, hollowed from tree trunk or made with a skin-covered frame, provided his limited means of transport. But the ancient Briton remained faithful to stone long after a knowledge of metallurgy in the Middle East heralded the Bronze Age; indeed, some axe manufacture may have persisted right on into the beginnings of the Iron Age—introduced into Britain by Celtic invaders about 500 BC. Only under the Romans did Celtic craftsmanship in iron really assert itself.

3

---·≈·---

The Invaders of Bath

WHEN JULIUS CAESAR was given the task of adding France to
the Roman Empire, he had no sights on Britain. But the
Britons, like the Gauls, were largely Celtic, and so they gave a
hand in defending their neighbours' territory against Rome. Julius
Caesar decided that the Britons should be punished for this and, in
55 BC, invaded Britain. Had Caesar been seeking a new province,
he would have brought larger forces: instead only a token assault
was made, and not until AD 43 did the Roman legions invade in
earnest. Even then the western extremities—Cornwall and
Wales—and all Scotland, were left much to their own devices.

The Romans appreciated the value of communications and they
built good roads, good bridges, and good settlements. Their main
road network ran from London to York, across to Chester, down
to Caerleon, then via Gloucester to Bath, on to Exeter, and back
to London. Exceptional were the extensions of Ermine Street
beyond York to Hadrians Wall, and of Watling Street through
Canterbury to Dover; and an important road linked London with
Colchester and Norwich. The Fosse Way running diagonally
from Lincoln to Exeter passed through Bath, which was probably
occupied under Emperor Claudius as early as AD 54. Here the
first target of the invaders was the mineral wealth of the Mendips,
where the Phoenicians before them had mined silver and lead,
near Cheddar. But the Romans were quick to appreciate the
nearby thermal springs which were to give Bath its connotations
of health and eventually of elegance, through the ensuing two
thousand years: its development as a spa dates from the time of

Agricola (AD 78–84) when the romanizing of Britain was a major domestic policy. It is clear now that the Romans installed a series of curative baths equalled only in their finest continental spas, and these were undoubtedly one of the wonders of Roman Britain (see Plates 1 and 2).

Though the Romans may thus be said to have founded the first civilized community at Bath, settlement in the neighbourhood before the Roman occupation is evident in the remains of earlier camps, such as Solsbury, in the surrounding hills. The origin of the town is attributed to the legendary Bladud, son of the King, Lud Hudibras, and father of King Lear, in the ninth century BC. (There would seem to be a disparity of some 1500 years between the Lears of Bladud and Shakespeare.) Prince Bladud, banished because of his leprosy, worked as a swineherd, and cured his disease by bathing in a "steaming swamp" close to the banks of the Avon. So grateful was he that on accession he brought his court to Bath, and converted the swamp into the hot baths discovered some nine hundred years later by the Romans.

Aquae Sulis was the name given to the small settlement by the Romans, and politically it was of little more significance than the name implies, at least during their early occupation. But perhaps cleanliness always attracted godliness: the heathen goddess Sul was patron of the springs, and Minerva was the Roman goddess of healing. As the springs had healing properties, what more natural than that the Romans should build within the compact twenty-five acres of the settlement a temple to Minerva? Traces of this work of the Romans, together with the elaborate series of baths designed during their four centuries of rule, have been slowly discovered during the last 250 years, and without doubt much remains yet to be uncovered.

Antiquarians had always believed that Minerva's Temple existed and that it would lie under the present Abbey church. The first evidence came in 1727 when a gilded bronze head of Minerva was unearthed during excavations for a sewer along Stall street. The head had been crudely hacked from the torso, suggesting typical Anglo Saxon treatment, and it is thought from the unfinished top of the head that originally a Corinthian helmet crowned Minerva's effigy (see Plate 2). It is certain that the head dates from the Roman occupation; the craftsman may however have been British. But the ruins of Minerva's Temple should they exist, remain locked under the Abbey Yard and under the Abbey itself.

The stone used in the construction of the Roman Villa at Box was taken from the quarries at Box Hill, but it is not possible to say with equal certainty whether the stone used in constructing the baths at Aquae Sulis came from Box Hill or Combe Down. It is known that the Romans favoured the very hardest stone called 'corngrit' for their buildings, and the fine state of preservation of the stone so far discovered in the baths complex proves the wisdom of their choice. Such stone is likely to have been quarried to the south of the City, near the Fosse Way, probably in the neighbourhood of present day Bloomfield Crescent, where the Brerewick Camp of the Romans was sited. Yet the size of some of the blocks in the baths suggest that they were mined at Box, or taken from the outcrop there.

For Bath, 1727 was a vintage year, for then a 21-year old architect from Yorkshire, John Wood (of the Nash-Allen-Wood triumvirate) settled in Bath with a determination to transform the City from one in which he said 'streets were become like dunghills and pig-styes' to one of palladian beauty. As the City was transformed, John Wood followed in detail the excavations which led to the discovery of the Roman baths. In July 1727, the workmen on the Stall Street sewer unearthed a tiled floor beneath which hollow box-tiles formed part of a hot air circulatory system at the west end of the Roman baths site. Soot in the tiles confirmed the conclusion that this was part of the furnace, or hypocaust, installed by the Romans for central heating.

The discoveries of 1727 had been important enough, but more were to come in 1755 when the Duke of Kingston's bath project was undertaken over the site of the old Abbey House. Excavations in the loose soil first revealed a Saxon cemetery and, underneath it, the east end of the Roman baths in an excellent state of preservation. Alas, by 1763 when the Kingston Baths were completed, the Roman remains were buried once more. Attitudes were very different two hundred years ago, and it will be realised that archaeology was not yet being treated with the respect it deserved. Even the discoveries during further drainage work some fifty years later were treated in the same way: between 1799 and 1803 work in Abbey Passage and Union Street revealed detail of vestibules on the north and south sides of the Roman bath site, and the overall dimensions of the baths could then be assessed at 130 × 300 feet.

James Irvine was primarily responsible for the subsequent successful excavation and restoration of the Roman baths: he obtained permission in 1867 to excavate, and in trials south of the Kingston Baths he exposed the remains of a room with a semi-circular bath. Four years later Irvine watched attentively as Major Davis, the Bath City Engineer and Architect, excavated in Abbey Passage to locate and stop a leak in the Kings Bath—one of three mineral baths dating from the days of the West of England wool industry. Once again Roman masonry was revealed, including the main steps leading to the Great Bath of the Roman complex. But these repair works interfered with water supplies to the Kingston Baths, and for that reason were abandoned. When, seven years later, the Kingston Baths were taken over by the City authority, work on the leak in the Kings Bath could be resumed. Davis unearthed the main drain and spring of the Romans Baths. At last public consciousness of the value of archaeology was dawning.

Reluctantly at first, Davis turned to the restoration of the baths, and this was accompanied by acrimonious argument on method and treatment between archaeologists and the City authorities for many years. In 1923 the Kingston Baths were finally demolished, enabling the archaeologist W. H. Knowles to direct further operations; his work resulted in the baths complex as seen by visitors today. But the story is unfinished. Professor Barry Cunliffe, perhaps the greatest living authority on Roman Bath, has said: 'Bath is on the brink of new discoveries which might revolutionize our understanding of the place and time: the next fifty years are likely to see more archaeological activity than perhaps any time in the City's past.'

Rome was sacked by the Goths in AD 410 and again by the Vandals in AD 455. The Roman Empire, which had succeeded in absorbing peacefully the nations it conquered, had nothing in common with the barbarians, who attacked from Germany, north and east Europe, and from Asia. Rome needed her legions to defend the long line of the Rhine and Danube, and to improve communications her Empire was divided between Rome and Constantinople; strangely the Eastern Empire survived for a thousand years after Rome fell. When the Roman legions in Britain were recalled early in the fifth century, they left behind them not only good roads, bridges, and camps, but a law-abiding people converted to Christianity—a people who had also been romanized by four centuries of interbreeding.

Next came the Anglo-Saxons, but these invaders, starting with the landing of Hengist and Horsa on the north coast of Kent, met considerable opposition, and their conquest of south-western Britain took well over a hundred years. Meanwhile Aquae Sulis went into a state of slow decay, for the processes of nature turned against her. Even before their departure, the Romans had found it necessary to build up the floor levels in the baths to offset inundations from the Avon river; and after they went, the floods came in, leaching the strength out of the foundations and walls, so that the stately baths slowly collapsed and sank into the mud.

Left much to themselves, the inhabitants continued their romanized way of life in Aquae Sulis in a community which must have deteriorated as the marsh took hold. But as with the Roman settlements at Cirencester and Gloucester, Aquae Sulis gradually became an administrative and market centre. Each had a local 'king', until in 577 at the Battle of Dyrham in the Cotswolds, the Britons were defeated by the Saxon Kings Ceawlin and Cuthwine. In came the Saxons, to rename Aquae Sulis as Akemancaester, 'the town of invalids', which shows that, baths or no baths, the hot healing spring waters were still used. It would have been at this time that Bath was sacked and destroyed. Dyrham was an important event in English history for by this victory the Saxons reached the Bristol Channel and divided the 'West Welsh' from the 'North Welsh'; thereafter these Britons, all of Celtic extraction, lived separately in Cornwall and Wales.

It is a strange anomaly that the Anglo-Saxons led Britain into two hundred years of chaos yet they brought with them the concepts of sovereignty and aristocracy. This derived from the relationship of chief to warrior and became the basis of nobility and feudalism; and it gave them a breadth of understanding which made possible their eventual conversion to Christianity. Bath fell only a dozen years before Augustine and his missionaries arrived from Holy Rome.

27

The story of St. Aldhelm, in the light of these antecedents, seems less of a legend than it is sometimes taken to be. Aldhelm, or Ealdhelm, was a churchman of the young Anglo-Saxon church which stemmed from Pope Gregory's dream of 'Angles converted to angels.' Educated at Malmesbury and Canterbury, Aldhelm became abbot of Malmesbury in *c*.673 and Bishop of Sherborne in 705. He was notable as a scholar and a writer of verses including riddles (these usually in Latin). John Aubrey, the Wiltshire antiquary, before his death in 1697 wrote: 'Hazebury quarre is not to be forgot. It is the eminentest freestone quarry in the West of England, Malmesbury and all round the Country of it. The old men's story is that St. Aldelme, riding over there, threw down his glove, and bade them digge and they should find great treasure, meaning the quarrey' (see Fig. A).

A. The St. Aldhelm glove was adopted by The Bath Stone Firms as their trade mark.

History does not relate whether Aldhelm went back for his glove, but he certainly had marked the spot, for he went on to build the Abbey at Malmesbury using stone from the Hazelbury Quarry on Box Hill. This might conceivably have been ferried most of the way to Malmesbury on rafts via the By Brook and Avon river. Stone from Hazelbury was again taken, early in the twentieth century, for much needed repairs to the Malmesbury

Abbey fabric. Aldhelm also built the church of St. Lawrence at Bradford-on-Avon—held by many to be the oldest remaining Saxon church in the country—using the same stone (see Plate 3).

It was at this time (taken as 676) that the first Abbey was built at Bath. However it was not necessary even to cross the Avon to old Brerewick camp for stone, for by this time there was ample stone lying around from the buildings either destroyed or decayed since the Roman occupation. The Abbey was founded by Osric, ruler of the province of Hwicce in the new Mercia.

From the time of Augustine's arrival in 597, the 'Rule' of the Italian St. Benedict—perhaps the most important formative document of medieval Christian civilization—had been central to the conversion of Britain and much of Europe to Christianity. Gregory was devoted to the Rule, and so the Benedictine monasteries in Britain came to be built. Over the three centuries of the existence of the old Abbey, many of these monasteries fell into decay, and it was King Edgar, son of Edmund, who revived them, urged on by St. Dunstan of Somerset and the Cluniac Benedictines at Mâcon. So the old Abbey was demolished and rebuilt as the Cathedral of St. Peter; and here came Edgar to be crowned the first King of all England in 973.

As Edgar had been King since 957, the deferred coronation has mystified some writers, but there may be two reasons for it. Firstly Edgar, who was only 14 years old when he became King of Northumbria and Mercia in 957, did not accede to the Kingdom of Wessex until his elder brother died two years later. Wessex had been defended successfully and successively against the Danes by Edgar's grandfather Edward the Elder; then by his uncle, Athelstan; then by his father, Edmund, and finally by his brother Eadwig who died at the age of 19 in 959. Secondly, there is no earlier reference to a coronation ceremony. Though 'investitures' had always been included in ceremonies ranging from those in the Bible to those of Imperial and Papal Rome, the elements of consent, consecration, enthronement and communion were new, and this Anglo-Saxon rite is attributed to St. Dunstan. Dunstan himself was born of a Wessex royal family, and became Abbot of his native Glastonbury (see Plate 3) After befriending Edmund, Dunstan was exiled by Eadwig, and it remained for Edgar, two years later, to recall Dunstan and consecrate him Bishop of Worcester; later Dunstan was translated first to London and finally to Canterbury.

It was the Anglo-Saxon Kingdom of Wessex, therefore, which finally provided a dynasty for a united England. The coronation at Bath was a unification not only for the state but also for the church; it was a show of strength to Wessex, and something of a personal triumph for Dunstan. Soon after the Bath ceremony, Edgar was again crowned at Chester, where all the eight kings in Britain—Scottish, Welsh, and Norse—came to acknowledge his supremacy. Edgar's protégé had indeed done well.

It is hard to believe that the cathedral of 957 was built entirely from the stone left in Bath by the Romans, much of which would already have been re-used. It is more likely that the monasteries developed their building prowess and commissioned the early quarrymen at Hazelbury and Combe Down to cut the stone they required, shaped more to suit the type of Saxon architecture already seen in Sherborne. St. Benedict and St. Wilfrid had already established a school of church building in England and Italian influences were notable. The Bath Cathedral of St. Peter may therefore have conformed to the new Anglo-Saxon pattern of high narrow nave and massive tower.

Bath had had no easy time, but in the hundred years following Edgar's coronation was given a short respite. The springs continued to emit mineral waters and Bath avoided direct attention. Instead, together with all England, Bath attracted direct taxation—in its most ignominious form. To buy off the Danes, danegeld was raised by the weak Ethelred the Unready; under Canute danegeld became a war tax; and even William the Conqueror drew up the Domesday Book to show the state how danegeld should be levied. The Lord of the Manor was personally responsible for raising this tax, and since he answered financially to the state he became the 'owner of the land and all who lived in it'. This practice, which reinforced feudalism, ruined the peasantry who often declined into serfs. Of King Rufus, son of William the Conqueror, historians have found little good to say. In the second year of his reign, the county of Somerset rose in revolt against him, and this led once more to the destruction of Bath, and the Cathedral of St. Peter with it.

In this year, 1088, John de Villula became Bishop of Wells; his appointment, having been made by Rufus, might have boded ill. But the new bishop, an apothecary from Tours, chose Bath from which to administer his see. It is said that for a consideration of some £500 he was granted the lordship of the manor as well as the abbey estates. More importantly he established the see of Bath and Wells which has survived to this day. For John of Tours, the healing waters of Bath were a bonus, and the town mint no doubt had its uses. He set about stripping the site of the old cathedral and building anew. This version, by every precept, had to be a Norman Romanesque cathedral priory of important size, and so it was, being more than 350 feet in length. The plan of the priory has been lost so that attempts at description are theoretical and possibly misleading; nevertheless when 300 years later the priory went into a state of decay, a Tudor Abbey—the one we have today—rose (through many vicissitudes) on its foundations, so that at least some evidence remains for posterity.

It took altogether about 200 years for the present Bath Abbey to be completed: two centuries in which kings and politicians, ably assisted by nature, interrupted, and often put into reverse, its building process. It was Oliver King, consecrated Bishop of Bath and Wells in 1495, who revived interest in the crippled cathedral. The new bishop had a dream of ascendant angels and a voice calling for the king to restore the church. He went one step further and decided to build a new though smaller abbey, appropriate to the needs of the town in Tudor England. And by clever planning, the old Norman foundations were used for the foundations of the new nave and choir and indeed of the tower itself (see Plate 4). Bishop King was enough of a politician to engage two court architects, William and Robert Vertue, for his work. William, an expert in the design of vaults, produced the great vault of the choir and the fan vaults in the aisles, 'than which', according to William, 'none was so goodly, neither in England nor in France' (see Plate 4). The new Abbey church called the 'Lantern of England' because of its huge exposure of windows lighting the nave, was the last great church to be built before the break with Rome. Henry VII wanted the new Abbey—and his statue, complete with arms and supporters, are contained in a niche.

But then came Henry VIII, who though successful in separating his Bishops and clergy from allegiance to Rome, failed to separate the monastic orders which were mostly international in origin. The dreaded Thomas Cromwell, 'Hammer of the Monks', set out to put down the monasteries and seize their property. The first Act of 1536 dissolved the 276 smallest of the 600 monasteries in the land. There followed first the abortive Pilgrimage of Grace of monks in Yorkshire, and then the ferocious attack on the larger monasteries ran home, culminating with the execution of the last Abbot of Glaston on Glastonbury Tor.

The greed of King and courtiers swallowed most of the spoil, estimated at one-quarter of the 'total rental of England', and about a thousand newly-rich families became the new aristocracy of England, many occupying the old abbeys, while other monastic and church buildings became 'quarries for new buildings', their lead roofs and treasures despoiled by the new possessors. Thus suffered the new abbey at Bath which was dissolved in 1539. Not until thirty-five years later when Queen Elizabeth I visited Bath on a progress through the western countries, was interest revived. The Queen was shocked by the state of the Abbey and sponsored a nationwide fund for its restoration. She also ordered the consolidation of the many Bath parishes into one with the Abbey as soon as it was restored. So restoration and completion work proceeded, albeit as slow as ever.

James Montagu, a favourite of King James I, was consecrated Bishop of Bath and Wells in 1608, and it was he who really saw to the completion of Bath Abbey. Within a matter of eight years it was roofed and fully equipped. It had been blessed with gifts in cash and kind, and had become a fitting place to receive the remains of Montagu when he died, Bishop of Winchester, in 1618. His elaborate tomb in the abbey pays ample tribute to the man who finally completed the job.

The Abbey today, by these various events in its history, is necessarily a mixture of stones quarried in the general area through some 1600 years, from the days of the Romans to the Tudors. The certainty is that all the stone came from the quarries at or between Combe Down and Box Hill, and perhaps in future archaeological projects it may be possible to identify the points of origin with exactitude. Most of this stone has now had two thousand years use under building stress and exposure to the elements: and much of it is none the worse for that.

4

Customs of the Manor of Portland

THE ROMAN OCCUPATION extended to Portland. The prime interest of the Romans in the area started at Radipole, now Weymouth, from which their camp at Dorchester was supplied. At first they crossed to Portland only to maintain a light on the Bill. History does not tell us whether the invaders mastered Chesil Beach or landed on the beaches of the Bill. Eventually they settled, and many artifacts remain to give evidence of their tenure (q.v.). They appreciated the value of the stone around them and set the natives to work in quarrying operations. This is evident from the very literal 'mark' they left behind them, which incidentally, survived well into the twentieth century. As the blocks of stone were quarried their cube was recorded by a series of cuts which are best explained by reference to Figure B (i), (ii) and (iii), in which, as an example, the number 37 is illustrated. In figure (i) the number 10 is represented three times by vertical lines cutting the horizontal line and making crosses, giving a total of 30: next the number 5 is represented by a half line drawn down to, but not crossing the horizontal line. Finally, two ones are added, to give the total of 37 cubic feet. It will be seen by the stages (ii) and (iii) (which have been added here purely for the development of hypothesis) that the marks have been separated and then turned, revealing an interesting similarity to conventional Roman numerals. The question begs itself: could these marks have stemmed from early quaternary cave markings, from which Roman numerals were later derived?

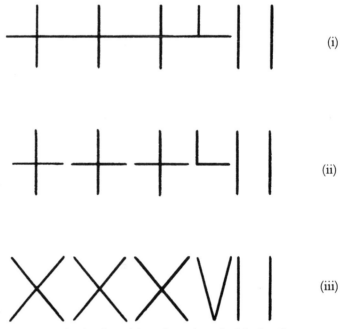

B. The Roman method of marking the cube of a block of stone.

Until recently (well after World War II) all stone quarried on the island was marked by this system (see Plate 5).

The Roman occupation gave Britain roads, bridges, strategic fortifications, and Christianity which had spread through the Roman Empire in the third and early fourth centuries AD. The Britons at first were sceptical and about the year 304 Alban became the first martyr to Christianity; yet in the four centuries of Roman rule the Britons became a civilized race and finally turned to Christianity in the fifth century. But when the Romans left, following the fall of Rome in AD 476, Britain was effectively left to the Britons, an event for which they were not ready: they were prey to the Picts and Scots beyond Hadrian's Wall, and by inviting the help of the Jutes as allies, they let new enemies in. The Angles and Saxons followed the Jutes, and over a period of 150 years, Britain was conquered—and became England.

In this process, the Britons, or most of them, were driven into the moors and mountain fastnesses of Cornwall, Wales and Cumbria, where their Celtic blood and instincts gave them the power of survival. But for Britain as a whole, 'England' was a setback which it took her several centuries to digest; Christianity lapsed except in Wales, and for a hundred years, England was pagan once more. Then came St. Augustine and forty monks from Rome to reconvert England to Christianity, and Ethelbert became England's first Christian king.

When Thomas Hardy described the Isle of Portland as the 'Gibralter of Wessex', he gave the Devil more than his due. Contrast the hot land-based Mediterranean rock of southern Spain with the treeless slab, ostracized by nature and cut off by the sea, one thousand miles to the north, and the simile pales. Portland, for whatever purpose God had in mind, was made to be as inaccessible and implacable as any place to be found in Britain. The Island rises from the sea, a forbidding block of solid stone; and stretching out from Bridport to meet it is the treacherous ghoulish finger of Chesil Beach that lures sailors to their death, dissevers mercilessly underfoot, vanishes in swirling eddies and mists, or cowers under the lash of gale and spume. Here, if anywhere on earth, you will hear the sea's

'. . . melancholy long withdrawing roar
Retreating to the breath
Of the night-wind down the vast edges drear
And naked shingles of the world.'

The fact that Portland is now joined to the mainland by a highway giving access in all but the worst weather, is a tribute to the stoicism of its small island race; for here a primitive community, disinclined to conform with the pattern of the outside world, has defied nature, lived its own life, made many of its own laws, and succeeded in its own way, through more than a thousand years. Call them a simple people and you will be wrong. They may not be much travelled: they know the fate of the traveller on their own shores. They may be superstitious: they have cause to be. They may not be great scholars: they have no need to be. What they do know, however, is the asset value of their strange island home which, for all its barrenness, has given the civilized world one of the most beautiful workable stones that earth has to offer. And they are content. They did not need to be deeply philosophi-

35

cal to realize that stone is heavy and that water is a means of transport; it will be seen that they developed their market accordingly.

The geographical position of Portland is such that it could not fail to figure in Britain's history; and though monarch and government used their power to make the islanders conform with general practice, they did so with limited success. The Britons of Portland before Roman occupation were by general pattern a mixture of indigenous cave men from the mesolithic epoch, Iberians who came from Europe in the neolithic epoch, and Belgae, the last Celtic invaders to gain a foothold in the south of Britain during the first century BC. These islanders lived at the dawn of history; they lived in villages, tilled the soil, grew corn, herded cattle and sheep, and prayed to heathen gods. Their priests, latterly the Druids, made laws, adjudicated in crime, wrote music and poetry, foretold the future, and offered sacrifices to the gods. Under their sway, the Britons were a peaceful people.

But paganism in Britain died for a time when the Druids were driven into Anglesey and slaughtered there under orders of the Roman Governor Suetonius. The fact that Boadicea, spurred on by the Druids, captured London, Colchester and St. Albans, and slew some 70,000 Romans while the scourge of the Druids was preoccupying the Roman Governor, is not just commonplace history; it is indicative of the dedication of the early Briton to his beliefs. When Suetonius turned on Boadicea, who earlier had been whipped by the Romans, she preferred suicide to captivity: alas, as a pagan she did not qualify for canonization, and in a later era she might well have earned a Duchy, or at least the George Cross.

Though comparatively little is known of the Dark Ages, it is significant that by the time Edward the Confessor died and William of Normandy succeeded him, a new civilization had emerged, with an administration sensible enough for William to adopt much of it. The period between the English conquest and the Norman conquest had set the scene for the feudal system.

The Saxon village (of wattle-and-daub dwellings) was always adjacent to arable land divided into two or three fields that lay fallow in alternate or successive years. These fields were divided into strips or 'lawns', usually of one acre in area, and each villager held a number of these strips, scattered among the fields for the fairer distribution of good and bad land: hence never together. The length of a strip was 220 yards, or the distance a team of oxen could draw the plough without stopping for rest; hence it was a furrow-long, or furlong. In a working day the team would plough this length to the width of a chain, or 22 yards. Hence the strip contained 4840 square yards, or one acre.

By communal agreement, similar crops were grown on the many strips in one field, and the dates of ploughing, sowing and harvesting would also be agreed. The villagers who worked primarily for survival, had little use of their little money, which paid the pedlar for articles such as nails, spices, and tar. This rural Anglo Saxon scene was rudely interrupted by the incursion of the Northmen, called Danes; these were intrepid seamen from Norway, who, through a series of successes and failures, eventually ruled England under Canute and Normandy under the dukedom ceded to them by the weak French King, Charles the Simple. Thus Northman, or Norman, blood was pulsing in noble veins on both sides of the English Channel as the eleventh century dawned.

The plundering of the Danes had already led the Anglo-Saxons to start giving up their strip-lands in return for protection by powerful neighbours. Canute divided England into four Earldoms, and thus the feudal system came about. The King was lord paramount, owning all land: his vassals were the great earls, or tenants-in-chief; they in turn had lesser nobles and lords of the manor, and under them were the villeins, all in turn being sub-tenants or vassals; all were called upon for military service and the villeins for work also. The lords of the manor gave back the strip-lands to the villeins in return for their fealty—the personal feudal tie between two people. Vassals were not serfs however, for every landowner other than the king was a vassal, and every vassal was a landowner.

When William came to the throne of England he accepted the concepts of feudalism, but he made certain modifications. Firstly, to avoid rivalry, he dissolved the four Earldoms created by Canute, and he then parcelled out to his Norman followers most of the lands of England, all of which had been forfeited to him at Hastings. But he was careful only to give small parcels, to make rebellion more difficult; and he kept about one-fifth of England for himself—the royal domain. Some lands he gave to the church, and these were held by bishops and abbots. Finally, after logging the names of all the new landowners in the Domesday Book, he rallied them on Salisbury Plain to take an oath of allegiance, that every landowner, from noble to lord of the manor, was bound to his King as well as to the person to whom he owed fealty as vassal. William decided that the Isle of Portland which Edward the Confessor had held before him, should remain royal domain, and he became Lord of the Manor. The Exchequer text of the Domesday Survey of 1086 bears this entry:

'The King holds the island which is called Porland. King Edward held it in his lifetime. There the King has 3 ploughs in demesne and 5 serfs and there 1 villein and 90 bordars have 23 ploughs. There are eight acres of meadow. There is pasture 8 furlongs long and eight wide. This manor with what belongs to it renders £65 blanched.'

The Exeter text of Domesday adds that 3 pack-horses, 14 beasts, 27 pigs and 900 sheep were already on the island.★

The Middle Ages had no set starting or finishing point, but it is generally accepted that this period covers about a thousand years from AD 500–1500. In the earlier centuries, the countries of Europe were lands of opportunity for the strong and the cunning, and rank was more important than nationality. The Baron, the Knight Errant and even the Crusader were concerned with particular, not general, causes; and owning land was more important than being English. Slowly, however a consciousness of nationality developed: the purpose of the Hundred Years War brought knights, men-at-arms and archers together as comrades. Pride of nationality developed, with hatred of enimical countries as nations rather than as individuals.

With this bonding of mutual interest between high and low in the land, England was the first country to turn away from serfdom; during the fifteenth century most villeins commuted

---

★ A serf was a slave, attached to and transferable with land; a villein was one holding land by a servile tenure; and a bordar was a cottager, working bord-land for the maintenance of his lords table, or board. 'Blanched' has two connotations: a blanch-holding was a tenure by which the tenant was bound to pay only a nominal rent; a blanch-farm was one for which the rent was payable in silver and not in cattle. Beasts in this instance must, by definition, mean oxen.

their work for an annual money payment and since they still held their strip lands, this payment became equivalent to a rent, at that time amounting to about sixpence per acre per annum. The villein thus paid the lord of the manor in coin by first selling his own produce, and the lord of the manor employed wage-labourers who lived in tied cottages, much as the bordars had done 500 years earlier. The feudal system was dead, but the strange Isle of Portland was not to be hurried. The island had a special case to plead, and would do so in its own unusual and often unique manner.

The survival of the manorial system on the Island, when the rest of the Kingdom had turned long since to local government by rural, urban, and county authorities, was more logical than it sounds. The Monarch was represented by the Court Leet. Within the limits of the island—there are but 2800 acres of it in all—the preservation of the Open Fields and Common Pastures was paramount to the balanced island economy, and enclosures were accordingly resisted, where necessary by force. This called for the continued existence of the Court Leet and its officers after the feudal system died: the Court was necessary to govern the complicated systems of property ownership and communal agriculture. The principles of property ownership, and particularly of division when renounced or bequeathed, though significant in the agricultural context, were vital to the quarrying industry that was to develop much later.

The sovereign has always been Lord of the Manor of Portland since the Norman invasion, and remains so today. A Crown Steward, usually a lawyer, represents the sovereign's interest. Historically, the Reeve, or Collector of Rents, was chosen at the Michaelmas Court meeting, and he was by court edict 'the Tennant who payeth the greatest Rent to ye Lord'; he enjoyed the free use of a piece of land known as the Reeve Plot. The office of Reeve could be held by a woman, and sometimes was, though a man was then appointed as her deputy.

Twenty-four jurymen served the Court. The collection of rents was recorded by marking them on the Reeve Staff, a four-sided pole which could be as much as 12 feet in length. A complicated system of notches and cuts showed the rent paid by each tenant. Five notches distinguished between the five hamlets: a hollow circle for Southwell, a cross in a circle for Wakeham, a cross between parallel lines for Weston, a 'W' for Easton and a 'V' for Chesil. There followed cuts and scratches representing the payment of 1/-, 6d, 1d, ½d and ¼d. Needless to say, a new Reeve Staff was required each year.

The origin of the rents paid by the islanders leads to a contradiction of terms, for though rent-paying, the tenants had become Freeholders. The 'rent' originally paid was a quit rent to commute for service and not a rent for the lease of land: with this explanation the Court Leet presentment of 1741 is more readily understandable:

> 'We present that all Tenants within ouer Mannor are Freeholders and ouer Rent is Certain Gathered by a Several Reeve every Year att Michaelmas by a Staff. This is an Antient Custom as will appear by ouer Rentall Staff.'

The Court Leet assisted the Freeholders in resisting enclosures, though it appears that the system permitted encroachments for which due payment of a fine could be made. The Jury went out after Michaelmas 'to throw down houses and walls when people would not pay what they were charged'.

Property on the Island changed hands by one of three methods: church gift; surrender at Court; and bequeathment on death. The ceremony of Church Gift (see Fig. 1 page 224), completed before two witnesses, had a ritual in simple but beautiful English:

> 'I (George Smith) came into the Parish Church of Portland and did there and then according to an ancient custom time out of mind freely give unto (John Brown) a yard and a half of Fine Ground situated and being within the Isle and Manor of Portland in Coomfield in a furlong called Above Broad Croft which said land as above mentioned I (George Smith) do give unto the said (John Brown) freely to give or to sell to him and his heirs for ever . . . with the yearly rent of one penny payable unto the Lord of the said Manor AND this being my free CHURCH GIFT In witness whereof . . . '

When property was transferred by Surrender at Court, the title was surrendered to the Crown Steward at Court Leet and passed on to the purchaser at the agreed price; but for a period of 'a year and a day' thereafter the heir to the seller could redeem the property at the agreed price, 'and hee to Enjoy the same to himselfe and his Heyres for Ever.' Under the surrender procedure, a fine called a Landchief was paid to the crown at the rate of three pence per acre. The division of property by will was recorded by the Court, and where a tenant died intestate his property was divided equally by the Court among sons, or being none, among the daughters, but saving a one third interest for the 'wife and Relict' of the deceased during her life. A duty or 'heriot' of two shillings and sixpence was also due to the Crown on the death of a tenant. Articles of Enquiry dated 1741 have it thus: 'At the death of every Tenant happens for a Reliefe 2/6 to his Majesty, This is a Custome.'

From time immemorial the striplands in the Common Fields had been handed down 'undivided' for to divide them would have reduced their size to uneconomic units. So through succeeding generations one strip would come to have many shareholders, and it became commonplace for a man to possess, for instance, 'the undivided quarter of the undivided third part of the undivided half of a strip'. As will be seen, when the quarrying of stone eventually encroached on old stripland, the business of establishing quarry titles became a lawyer's paradise.

Over the rock face of the island is a mantle of soil averaging no more than a foot in depth—one reason why there are hardly any trees on the island. Said John Leland, in the sixteenth century 'There be very few or utterly no trees in the isle, saving the elmes about the chirch.' Agriculture had always been the island's main industry, however, and for warmth in the winters, dried animal manure was substituted as a fuel for the wood that the island lacked. This in turn deprived the land of fertilizer, and Portlanders therefore worked their land on a 'two-field' system, in which one field lay fallow in alternate years, reducing their annual product to half its potential. The strange custom of 'chamber-lye' thus evolved, in which all urine made in winter was saved in casks for distribution over wheat crops in spring and summer. ('Lye', an old word for fertilizer, usually related to alkalies such as potash.) Some care had to be taken in the use of it, but applied at the right time it contributed to bumper wheat crops.

In addition to the Open Fields there were areas of Common

Pasture or grazing land, sited on the Bill and along the Clifftops, and on the Verne at the island's summit. It was the business of Haywards (there were about six chosen at the Court Leet each year) to see that when the arable fields were cropping, they were fenced off to keep cattle out. By edict of the Leet, individual strip tenants had to conform to common dates for sowing and reaping their crops, for the date set by the Court on which cattle could be turned onto the stubble effectively finished harvesting. Again there was a maximum number of cattle allowed each tenant according to the size of his property. Any surplus cattle put out into the field over this allowance, or 'stinte', were to be forfeited to the Lord of the Manor. However as fines were substituted for forfeiture, the island became greatly overstocked.

Portland sheep had been kept on the island at least since the tenth century AD, and according to the experts, had not been crossed with other breeds. These animals were small with close fine wool, had black noses and yellow legs, and made fine-flavoured mutton. A letter from John Wilkes, pioneer of the freedom of the press, addressed to John Garrard's son Michael, the King's Purveyor on Portland, pays handsome tribute to Portland mutton:

Sir,   Grosvenor Square,
                                               October 1st, 1796.

I wish you now to begin to send me as in former years once in ten days or a fortnight a Portland sheep provided it be always very small and delicate. I think it will be better for you to pay the carriage and charge it to my account. Your county is remarkable for well-flavoured game. I should be glad if the hamper with the mutton might sometimes contain pheasants, or partridges or a hare or young wild ducks, plovers, woodcocks, snipes etc. for my table. I would pay the best price and keep "the secret". It might be an advantage to some of your acquaintance as well as convenient to me.

I am sir your most humble servant.

John Wilkes.

P.S. My daughter is fond of landrail,* if you had any of that bird as I hear there are plenty in your county.

Whether the size of Portland sheep was a matter of genetics or could be accounted for by the poor grazing on the Island—especially for the overcrowded sheep population—is not known. Either way Portland mutton was prized by epicures until in the nineteenth century the grazing land was ceded and sheep farming ceased.

One further custom, if it may so be called, that marked Portlanders as exceptional and isolated in their attitudes to the outside world, affected child-bearing. Portlanders rarely married strangers from the mainland—who were called 'kimberlins'. Inter-marriage was therefore prevalent, and fertility was regarded seriously by the hard-working sons of the Portland soil, for they wanted sons to follow them. It thus became almost formal procedure for marriage to be deferred until courtship resulted in pregnancy. If after a lapse of time the woman failed to conceive, the relationship ended. The Parish register between 1753 and 1803 shows that on average over 50% of all marriages were followed by baptism of progeny within nine months; it also shows that illegitimacy on the island was rare at a time when elsewhere in England it was a serious social problem. In many of these strange customs of Portland there can be discerned the Saxon theme, and it seems that the Portlanders shook off the Roman yoke as another intrusion of kimberlins and reverted to paganism. As part of the peoples of Wessex, the Portlanders were to be among the last in the land to accept Christianity.

---

* The corncrake.

5

Doulting and Wells

THE MISSIONARIES OF Holy Rome landed in 597 at Ebbsfleet in Kent, and strategically it was from Canterbury that England was reconverted to Christianity. It is almost incredible that the courage and vision of Gregory the Great was strong enough to force the doubting Augustine back into the shades of once-Roman Britain on such a daring enterprise. King Ethelbert and his kingdom of Kent were the first to be converted, closely followed by Essex, Middlesex, Surrey and Sussex. Augustine became the first Archbishop of Canterbury, and before his death in 604, had confirmed bishoprics in London and Rochester; it was a good foothold, and there, for a quarter of a century, the matter rested.

Then, by happy chance, Edwin of Northumbria wished to marry Ethelbert's Christian daughter Ethelburga. She travelled north, taking with her Paulinus, a priest who converted Edwin and Northumbria to Christianity, and Paulinus became the first Bishop of York. But Edwin and his successor Oswald, a Celtic Christian, were in turn killed in wars with the heathen King Penda of Mercia; so that Christianity lost its hold there. Only when Oswald's brother Oswy met and killed Penda at the Battle of Winwood was Christianity finally accepted in Northumbria; paganism slowly died throughout Mercia and even more slowly throughout Wessex. At the Council of Whitby, in 664, it was decreed that Northumbria should forsake Celtic Christianity for Roman Christianity, and thereafter all England had one church—three hundred years before all England had one King.

In 668 Theodore of Tarsus was consecrated Archbishop of

Canterbury, and he brought with him from Rome the African Hadrian. Both were great scholars who ensured that Canterbury became a school for Latin and Greek. Tarsus was a strong man and against fierce opposition, created a number of bishoprics; eventually—after his death—the work he had started led also to the system of parish churches, each with a parish priest.

At about this time the Christian mission of secular canons at Wells was established under King Ine of Wessex. Originally there were 50 canons; today there are 48. The original mission building dating from 704 was probably of wattle and daub construction though Aldhelm, who had advised Ine, is known to have worked also in stone. The influences of Rome were seen in the growth of ecclesiastical architecture, which used stone in contrast with the contemporary wattle and daub. The remains of Roman cities provided 'ready-hewn quarries' of squared stone for the purposes of the Saxon church building programme. The style of these Saxon churches was a romanesque combination of German and Rhenish architecture.

Building in the eighth century required finance just as it does today, and for this the church levied the tithe, or tenth, of the gross produce of the soil to satisfy its various needs. The tithe raised the church to a university of art, learning, architecture and civilization; but in the process, the tithe took many farmers back from freedom to serfdom. The bishops encouraged the growth of secular—non monastic—clergy, and in this way achieved direct control, for the monasteries were international in their foundation. Between the bishops and the monasteries, the Kings of Britain were persuaded—for the good of their souls—to part with vast lands as gifts, and were taught how to will even more of their possessions to the church at their death. The church gained its early wealth in this way, and with the wealth came power. Using its almost unique gift of literacy, the church committed the traditional law of the Kings of Britain to writing. As a result, one shire court, in which the bishop sat with the shire reeve, or sheriff, administered both spiritual and temporal laws. The young Christian church was solidly established, and was to remain so despite many challenges in the centuries that followed.

The three springs which give Wells its name rise to the east of the cathedral, but it was a fourth spring, the Well of St. Andrews, closer to the cathedral, that prompted the selection of the site of the early mission and the two cathedrals that were to succeed it. The three springs flow into the moat of the thirteenth century Bishop's Palace, to the south of the cathedral, and thence on through the yards and gardens of the little town, to join the Sheppey river at Coxley. The waters of the Well of St. Andrews, however, still run through an ancient mole under the camery and cloisters of the cathedral. The line of the mole suggests that it may have brought water to the font in the old Saxon cathedral.

No known traces remain of the original mission station, but parts of the foundations of two ancient buildings under the camery——immediately to the east of the cathedral cloisters—were unearthed in 1890. The more recent of these buildings, which had been erected against the cloister wall, was identified as the fifteenth century perpendicular chantry chapel built by Bishop Stillington.

It was Stillington, the archetype of fearless churchmen, who in 1483 denounced Edward V as the illegitimate child of Edward IV's bigamous marriage to Elizabeth Woodville, so that Richard III instead was acclaimed heir to the throne. Little wonder therefore that Henry VII (who wished to marry Elizabeth of York) committed Stillington to the Tower on the day following Richard's death two years later at Bosworth. But that was not enough: mercifully released from the Tower, Stillington again found himself imprisoned—at Windsor—for siding with Lambert Simnel against Henry—and this time, according to most accounts, it was for life.

Stillington had been Keeper of the Privy Seal since 1460 and was Chancellor of England from 1467 to 1475. He was consecrated Bishop of Bath and Wells in 1466, but only once visited Wells during his 26 years reign. On that occasion it was reported to the Dean and Chapter that the old Lady Chapel by the cloister was *ruinosa et defectiva*, and a new Lady Chapel was approved; the first Consistory Court was held in Stillington's Chapel in 1488. But the new Chapel was destined for a short life of 64 years. Its endowments were appropriated by the Crown under the Chantries Act, and it was agreed that Sir John Gates, a King's Collector of Lead, should remove the lead roof in 1552 on condition that the whole building be demolished, leaving no traces of its site above ground.

In the last 90 years the foundations of Stillington's chapel under the camery have been twice exposed, and the majority of the foundation stone has been attributed to Doulting quarry. It has also been shown that the mole from St. Andrews' Well was diverted when Stillington's chapel was built, to run round its south side. Beneath the remains of Stillington's chapel were the foundations of the chapel of the Blessed Mary, which also abutted the cloister wall, but was constructed at an angle of 12° divergence from the cloister right-angle. This building was used as the first Lady Chapel of the present cathedral.

These early foundations are of interest for several reasons. The strange angle of divergence from the line of the present cathedral may be explained by the early and essentially English concept (probably dating from Druid sun-worship) of pointing the nave of every church to the east. At the time this first cathedral was built there was no compass, and 'east' was determined by the sunrise at midsummer; but as the direction of the sun at sunrise depends on the relative altitude of the horizon, 'east' was only an approximation. The present cathedral is built to a more accurate east-west line, but the angle of divergence is still about 3°.

It has been suggested that the line of the old streets of Wells and of the buildings on the north side of the cathedral, including the Hall and Vicars Close, reflect the direction of the early churches, but this may not be so. Examination of the cathedral walls shows that the ground around the cathedral has at some time been levelled, and it is probable that the ancient buildings may simply lie along the original contour of the Mendips.

Although the chapel of the Blessed Mary abutted the cloister wall it was in fact part of an earlier cathedral, sited mainly where the cloister garth stands today. This early cathedral was mostly demolished to enable the cloisters to be built, but the severed part (in the camery) was preserved and then joined up to the new east wall of the cloister. When the foundations were again exposed in 1978, it was revealed that aisles had been added to the original Lady Chapel, probably in the late fifteenth century.

Wells Cathedral on which building started about AD 1180, is formed mainly of Doulting stone (called Inferior Oolite because it lies in a lower natural bed than the Oolite of Bath). The few surviving records of Glastonbury Abbey show that the Doulting quarry was their possession (see Plate 3). The choice of Doulting stone for Wells is significant, for stone from the Bishop's manor at

Chilcote was virtually 'on the doorstep'; also the Chilcote Conglomerate, locally termed 'bastard freestone', is very hard and, unusually, can be 'laid against the bed' (i.e. laid face-bedded or end-bedded), thus being more adaptable in use. The surface of Chilcote stone is pock-marked, however, and compares unfavourably with Doulting which has a smooth surface and a superlative warm rich colour. Where the medieval custom was to plaster over irregular or pitted stone surfaces, with Doulting stone it was evidently sufficient to use a limestone wash.

The register of Walter de Monyngton, Abbot of Glastonbury from 1342 to 1375, survives and rests in the British Museum. From it we know that in 1354, the thirteenth year of his rule, Monyngton, granted to William de Cammel, Canon of Wells, 40 wain loads of freestone for building the new Chorister's House, and 20 loads for an unspecified purpose; and in the following year, at the instance of the Dean and Chapter of Wells, allowed fifty wain loads to be taken for the repair of the great bell tower of the cathedral church.

Nine years later Walter de Monyngton at the request of the Bishop of Bath gave permission for the taking of freestone '*signanter de petra in petram*' as it lay 'in the place where the workmen of Whategh last left off, southward to that place where the workmen of the said church (of Wells) have dug at other times.' The officers of the abbey were to keep a 'tale' (hence tally) of the loads of stone removed. They went also 'thrice in the week at least' to inspect the Wells quarrymen and take care that they did no damage to the abbot's quarry but dug lawfully (*pure*) and within their proper bounds. If, however, in spite of precautions any damage was done, the stranger workmen must pay for it (*sufficienter emendent*) before they left. In 1457, 12d per main load was the rate of carriage from Doulting to Wells Cathedral and at that time Robert Prusshe the quarrier was propitiated with a gratuity (*in rewardo*) of 20d beyond his wages.

Right up to the time of the Dissolution, Glastonbury derived a considerable profit from the quarries at Doulting, for in the account of this manor for 26–27 Henry VIII (the eleventh year of the last abbot martyred on Glastonbury Tor), £2.5s.5½d was received from the issues of the freestone quarry there beyond the expenses incurred '*in extraccione earundarum liberarum petrarum*'.

The Dean and Chapter of Wells resorted to the use of the

Chilcote Conglomerate as a means of ekeing out supplies from Doulting, which had always been difficult; for it was ever necessary to apply to the Abbot at Glastonbury for Doulting stone, whether for construction or repair work. In April 1381, the Vicar of Doulting, Henry Parker, with the consent of the Abbot, leased part of his glebe land as a quarry to the Wells Chapter. This field, known as Estheyfurlong, had an area of about 4165 square yards, lying on the north side of the road from 'Doulting to Chevelynch'; and for it the Chapter paid an annual rent of '18d at Easter', in later years compounded to 20 shillings. This quarry, at Chelynch, was worked through nearly six centuries until finally the quarry now known as Chelynch closed in 1967. The probability is that wagons bearing stone from Doulting to Wells would never have had to climb more than 30 feet to run straight into Dinder and thence to the Mason's Yard at the cathedral.

The earliest methods of winning stone from the Doulting quarries are unrecorded, but what evidence remains suggests that the principles of splitting by wedges, leverage with bars and lifting with hand-operated derricks, have been utilised since the Roman church builders arrived in Britain during the seventh century AD. Nothing occurred subsequently to make the life of the quarryman easier until steam, harnessed in the late nineteenth century, provided a source of mechanical power. It was then used primarily as a lifting force.

Up to the beginning of the twentieth century, the quarries at Doulting had been worked by hand. There were four quarries in all: three of them, Doulting, Chelynch and a small quarry operated by Percy Gane, were on the north side of the road from Shepton Mallet to Frome; and Brambleditch, now lost and forgotten, was on the south side. Brambleditch was off the Evercreech road, close to the railway line, and its cavities have now been filled with refuse by the cidermakers of Shepton Mallet.

After removal of the overburden, the stone to be cut was measured off and marked in black using a wooden straight edge. This mark would run parallel with the rock face at a required distance from it. A narrow flat-bottomed trench would then be cut along the black line, using first a jad and then a standback, two types of pick purpose-designed for the quarrying trade, after which the jad was used to cut lifting holes on the face side of the trench. The rock was then prised away by setting a wedge between chips (similar in function, but not in design, to the 'plug and feathers' used in other parts of the country) in the trench, and hammering the wedge home. The block of rock so loosened ran between one natural gully and the next. The gullies were usually about four to ten feet apart, and varied in width between two and twelve inches. Sometimes the block to be taken would run from a gully to an intermediate vent or fault. The block was then 'shaken out' by rocking with 'handy bars'—long iron bars with lever ends which could weight up to five hundredweight and require two or three men to handle. It was a common practice to set a handy bar in position and balance heavy rocks upon it in the evening, by which means the heavy prising was done overnight by nature, ready for the next day.

Originally the lifting had to be done by hand using dogs and a hand crane or derrick (the 'lewis' was never used at Doulting). But then came the steam crane and—at Doulting—there came also an innovation to break out the stone. This was a machine, remembered as the 'Chandler' (probably a corruption of 'channeller') or affectionately as the 'Jenny Jumper' which was steam powered and ran on its own four wheels along the track laid for it. Drills at each side of the Chandler made parallel cuts into the stone, so that two stretches along the rock face were cut at once. The Chandler mounted its own steam boiler to drive a spindle on which by a *cam* action, the drills were first lifted and then hammered into the rock as the machine moved along. The force of the drills meeting the rock caused Jenny to jump which apparently she did to good purpose. But when one day she was being lifted by crane from one track to another the lifting chain broke, and Jenny crash-landed in a state of total disrepair. She had made her last jump, and the process became manual once more. Conditions for the quarrymen were never easy. They were paid an hourly rate, and as recently as the 1920's, £3 was good take-home pay for a hard week's work. There was no pay in wet weather, 'nor even if it looked like raining.'

Stone from Doulting and Chelynch was loaded on to wagons that ran down by gravity to the mason's shop on the Doulting siding of Cranmore station. The wagons were drawn in pairs on a tramway, in the charge of two men. One man operated the brakes, the front wagon having a sprag brake and the rear wagon an elementary type of disc brake brought into contact with one front and one back wheel by a long racheted arm. The second, a groom, led a horse which accompanied the wagons, as the horse was needed to draw the wagons back to the quarry. They might do six journeys a day, and for the right to cross the Shepton Mallet-Frome road, the quarry-owners paid the local authority three shillings and sixpence per annum.

The crossing was not without hazard, and it was the duty of the groom to halt traffic on the road by waving a red flag. There were two reasons why the wagons had priority. Firstly it was extremely difficult, if not impossible, to stop the wagons when loaded on their downhill journey; and secondly, if the horse were stopped on his uphill journey, it was equally difficult, if not impossible, for him to start up again. And so eventually the inevitable happened. Despite the most furious flag-waving, a car driven by a schoolteacher from neighbouring Evercreech drove into the horse and put him down with some injuries. Fortunately there was one independent witness, a tramp (colloquially 'one of Johnny Wobbler's gang'), who was rewarded for remaining to give his account of the affair to the police. But the village policeman commented (with justifiable confidence): 'You needn't worry, the driver already hit a police car in Liverpool last week!' The horse, which had been hired from a neighbouring farmer, was put on the sick list for six months during which the insurance company paid ten shillings a week compensation and damages—shared equally between farmer and veterinary surgeon.

At Cranmore the stone was lifted by a steam gantry which straddled the railway siding (where the East Somerset Railway now has its engine shed), and the cutting and carving of stone was done in the shop there. Blacksmiths or iron masons fashioned the tools, and banker masons cut the stone using cross-cut saws (requiring two sawyers) and singlehanded 'frig-bobs'. A boiler drove a multiple set saw with upright saws bolted top and bottom. Iron masons also did rough work, and banker masons the finishing.

The era of Cranmore probably started from the early 19th century and lasted up to the late 1930's. During its closing years some 52,000 cubic feet of Doulting stone was shipped to Guildford Cathedral, and substantial quantities went also to Bury St. Edmunds Cathedral and Lancing College Chapel. The maximum recorded load was 250 cubic feet on one articulated lorry, which at a density of about $1\frac{1}{4}$ cwt per cubic foot of stone represents a load of about 16 tons.

The building of Wells Cathedral began at the critical time, AD 1180, separating Norman and Gothic architecture. Wells has many beautiful examples of plate and bar tracery typical of the first (Early English) Gothic period. The nave and central tower were completed in the thirteenth century; these, with the superb West Front, had been built before the cathedral was consecrated in 1239. By 1340 the Quire had been added, and in 1338 the graceful and effective inverted arches were erected to reinforce the central tower which had cracked and started to lean noticeably—a defect which can be seen today in the roof's dipping string courses. The south-west and north-west towers were built late in the fourteenth century, and in the next hundred years the cathedral was completed with its cloisters, Chain Gate and Penniless Porch (see Plates 6–9).

The oolite of Doulting was principally used in the construction, and there is an interesting contrast between the soft cream tones of this stone within the cathedral and the deeper red-brown tints where it has weathered on the exterior. Many other stones were used for particular purposes, including shafts of Blue Lias (quarried at Street), and of Purbeck and Kilkenny marbles. Tufa, somewhat like pumice, was used for vaulting the Chapter House, Lady Chapel and retroquire. Bath stone was worked for some of the better carvings on account of its softer, finer texture, but practically all the capitals and statues on the West Front are Doulting.

Today the stone of the West Front bears testimony to the wrath of the iconoclasts. The seventeenth century Parliamentarians mutilated or destroyed significant statues and those they could easily reach, in their campaign of obliteration and abscission. And 800 years of weather in all its extremes, together with the chemistry of a polluted atmosphere, have also taken their relentless toll. To resist further decay, an extensive programme of preservation has been progressing during the 1970's; to contribute to this effort, the silent quarries at Doulting were again opened to

Wells Cathedral. Chapter House steps.

Montacute House (above) and Brympton d'Evercy (below) are supreme examples of work in stone from Ham Hill.

Masterpieces of the masters. (Above) Christopher Wren's St Paul's Cathedral from the south-east, and (below) Inigo Jones's Banqueting Hall in Whitehall. Each is built in Portland stone.

A dramatic silhouette of St. Paul's Cathedral, circa 1950.

St Paul's Cathedral: (above left) the west entrance, (above right) cross, lantern and dome, (right) base of the north-west turret.

Wren's fascination for the dome is seen in several City churches. (Above) St Stephen's Walbrook, and (below) St Mary at Hill.

The memorial window to Christopher Wren in the Church of St Laurence Jewry also features Grinling Gibbons, the wood carver and Edward Strong, Wren's chief mason at St Paul's.

The Monument was designed by Wren to commemorate the Great Fire of 1666. (Inset) the head in flaming gilt, 200 feet above Billingsgate. (Above) aerial view. Again Wren used Portland stone.

provide selected stone to replace badly weathered masonry now accessible on the scaffolding network. Here masons work side by side with specialists who, by applying a lime poultice, are hardening the stone surface for the future while putting back the lime leached out in the past.

The quality of carving of the near-400 statues and other sculptures on the West Front has been acknowledged to make Wells the equal of Notre Dame, Amiens, Reims and Chartres; and certainly the finest in England. The cathedral was raised to the glory of God by man's imagination and endeavour, and the humble quarrymen and masons who made this possible could ask for no finer monument in which to dissolve their identity.

6

---※---

The Little Parishes of Ham

SOME FORTY MILES south of Doulting, at Hamdon, lay another cache of oolitic limestone, but one with a very different history. Whereas the Doulting quarries had been possessed by Glastonbury Abbey as early as the eighth or ninth century and were thereafter used exclusively for religious building, the quarries in the region of Hamdon, after serving the Romans with road stone, lay fallow for some thousand years. Only after the Dissolution of the Monasteries is there record of renewed activity, and then it was to provide building stone for the new gentry.

The hill called Hamdon, or shortly Ham, towers above Stoke, Montacute, Coker, and Chinnock, a few miles west of Yeovil. Below this cockpit of Somerset, a vista of England merges into the mists of Devon, Dorset, Hampshire and Avon. Strange man-made shapes survive in the dingles on the hilltop, relics of activities both ancient and modern that have contributed to England's beauty and glory; strange shapes, wreathed in a mystery and romance befitting their remoteness from the hustle of the highways that surround them.

As the Romans forged down from Bath towards Exeter, the outcrop of buff, iron-tinctured shelly limestone which they found at Ham was a godsend. It helped to make the Fosse Way, which ran on from Ilchester, passing within a mile of the hill. And as the road stretched forward, the stone provided the raw material for new settlements in the network of Roman occupation. The limestone crops out in the three parishes of Stoke, Norton-sub-Hamdon and Montacute, though it is probable that the quarries of

54

Stoke and Montacute were not worked until well into the Middle Ages. The Romans certainly concentrated their activities in the quarry on Ham Hill, and in the museum at Dorchester there may be seen a Roman coffin wrought from the stone of 'a well-opened quarry on the slopes of Hamdon.'

How long the quarry at Ham had been worked before the Roman occupation is a matter for conjecture; the Romans may have been attracted to the Hill by virtue of a pre-existing stone industry, or they may have happened upon the stone by chance when the hill was scaled for the purposes of survey. Few signs of settlement at Ham remain, but the small dish at the summit known as the Frying Pan is generally assumed to have been the amphitheatre in which the Romans held their games; and archaeological digs round about the same site have revealed an assortment of Roman coins, weapons, pottery and harness.

The hill appears to be one great mound of sand and fragmented shells compressed into layers of golden brown oolitic limestone. Though the band of stone runs from Bradford Abbas, south of Yeovil, through the holloways of Stoford to East and West Coker and so up to South Petherton, no other quarry has produced either the quantity or quality of the stone from Ham Hill. It is evident that the old workings were comparatively shallow, for the most workable building stone lay under a heading of rubble and thin layers of hardstone, and this hardstone was used to produce the tiles later used in the better quality medieval buildings.

The era of Saxon rule which followed the Roman occupation brought with it a simplicity and beauty in stone-carving that influenced sculpture over the next thousand years. From the Norman period onward for some 500 years, Ham stone was not only used locally, as in Montacute House and Sherborne Almshouse, but made its way to Cerne, Ford and Lyme Regis and to Bridgwater and Taunton. Ham stone was sometimes used together with the freestone of Doulting and rougher material from local quarries, as for example in the walls, now levelled, of Castle Cary.

The problems of transporting the stone were resolved by the use of rivers. H. J. Hunt, in a treatment of the 13th century building account of Taunton Castle, says 'The carriage of stone by water from the quarries down the river Parrett and then up the

Tone to Ruishton within the Manor of Taunton and only two miles from the Castle, indicates an early use of these rivers for navigation.'

When William the Conqueror called the Earls and Squires of England to Salisbury Plain, most of the lands ceded to him were reallocated, the church being one of the principal beneficiaries. But forest lands were retained. In this way much land in Somerset, including the present parishes of Stoke, Hamdon and Montacute, fell to the King and so to the Duchy of Cornwall as crown lands.

There can be little doubt that the early stone masons were all journeymen, who by moving to carve stone at its destination spread a common knowledge of quarrying and mining methods throughout the Oolitic regions. The origin of the word journeyman is often misunderstood. It derives from the French 'journee', meaning literally 'hired by the day' and thus no longer apprenticed and bound to serve for a period of years. It became practice for a journeyman mason to live near a quarry where he understood the characteristics of its particular stone, but to travel with the dressed stone to the site where it was to be carved and incorporated in a building; being paid not by the quarry proprietor but by the architect or principal of the new building. At Ham the time honoured method was to cut the stone into grooves with a pick (using the joints, or vertical fissures, where possible to save part of the work); then the stone was lifted from its natural bed by wedges driven under by sledge hammers, and shaken out with the use of heavy iron bars. This enabled a chain to be positioned, by which the block was lifted on to tramways in the early days by derrick and rachet, and latterly by steam power.

The workable stone at Ham was capped by an overburden of sand called 'ochre' and by inferior hardstone about 40 feet thick, both of which had first to be cut through. Thus the principal quarries came to be about 90 feet deep from the surface to the basement bed—or 'clout' as it was termed by the quarrymen. By the sixteenth century certain customs attached to the system of apprenticeship were observed. Payment of one shilling was extracted from apprentices on signing their indentures, and again when half way through their term were they to marry. Fines were inflicted when they allowed stone to fall off a banker when at work, or for working an undercut straight through a quoin, which was called 'cutting its throat'. As with the Purbeck marblers, Shrove Tuesday was a traditional festival when apprentices might claim a half day's holiday.

Even in the fifteenth century the cost of transporting stone had equalled its purchase price, and the superior stone was therefore used only for architectural features, and was supplemented by local stone for the main structure. This is observed in Richard Rochelle's accounts of the building of the Sherborne Almshouse, begun in 1439, where 'a quarry on site provided the main fabric but the windows, door frames, and dressings were of the more costly Ham stone'. From quarries 10 miles west of Sherborne came 51 Cartloads at 12d. a load, the cost of cartage being 1s. 8d. a load, whereas for the freestone from Hamdon, stone for six windows cost 1s. 10d. each and for two others 5s. each and 48 foot of the same freestone for three door frames cost 3d. per foot. The apparently well-ordered terms of these transactions presaged the rise of the Craft Guilds, which survived for some 200 years up to the Dissolution of the Monasteries, and were in England among the earliest combinations of workmen which were later to become trade unions.

We know that by the 15th century a number of quarrymen held their land from the Crown, and certain yeomen farmers had the right to quarry stone and wood within the Lord's Manor as had been the custom 'time without memory'. Ten quarries at Stoke were already so leased in 1456, and 20 years later 14 more quarries were opened and let for an annual rent of 4d. each. The Abbot of Ford was a lessee. One quarry was described as a 'hoterell quarraria petratum' called Jopesboure, and another, 24 foot square, a 'quarraria lapidarum', for which a new tenant, Arnold Croftman, had paid an entry fine of 6s. 8d. The total income from the Stoke quarries between 1515 and 1545 was 3s. 4d. per annum. Distant days!

There is no express reference to quarrying in Montacute earlier than the sixteenth century, although 'a freemason of the parish' is recorded in 1499, and 'Thomas Wilkins of Montacute in 1540 left to John Morley, mason, his workshops in the quarries of Hamdon'. This coincides with a new era that was overtaking England. The Dissolution of the Monasteries and the putting down of the

Guilds brought major church building projects to a halt, and in their place came the construction of manor houses fitting for the rising class of landholders and merchants. Thus we have Barrington Court built for the first Earl of Bridgwater 'extremely attractive, with its warm Ham Hill stone walls covered with lichen and its triangular gables and twisted finials"; and Brympton d'Evercy built for the Sydenhams, the house with its outbuildings, garden, chantry house and church being 'one of the most perfect the country has to offer' (see Plate 10). These with Melbury House, home of Sir Giles Strangways and Clifton Maybank, seat of Sir John Horsey, were all built in the first half of the 16th century and 'formed the core of a group of architecturally inventive houses, with barley-sugar finials and octagonal angle-shafts, their faces hollowed, which were designed by a master-mason or masons based at Ham Hill.'

With the coming of the 17th century the Phelips family had plans to build Montacute House. William Arnold, who had designed Dunster Castle and Wadham College Oxford was retained in 1590 by Sir Edward Phelips to conceive a house 'befitting the Speaker of the House and Master of the Rolls' (see Plate 10). And then came Chantmarle in Dorset, where John Joseph and Daniel Rowe of Hamdon were the principal masons, and Gabriel Moore the surveyor. In 1625 Sir Robert Phelips leased off land measuring 20 by 40 feet 'newly bound out' on Ham Hill adjoining the east part of the quarries, to make two quarries. The lessee, Richard Frye of Stoke, who paid 12d. a year, was given 'liberty to lay his rubbish' in the waste ground of Norton Hill.

These and others similar, were the quarries upon which Thomas Gerard happened on his journeys through England. In 1633 he described Ham as 'the goodliest quarry of freestone I ever saw', where 'masons tried cases of trespass in their own court in a pretty kind of commonwealth'. The quarries, said Gerard, were 'rather little parishes than quarries. So many buildings have they under the vast works to shelter themselves in wet weather, and their wrought stone in winter.' By 1697 nine quarries were being worked in the manor: John Clarke had three and 'three were in hand'. Each was 18 feet square and the annual rent usually £6.

Though there is little early record of the quarries at Stoke they had been 'very famous far' until they ceded pride of place to the quarries of Norton early in the 17th century. Despite the more fashionable Ham stone, however, they were still leased to the Phelipses of Montecute by the Duchy of Cornwall in the eighteenth century, and 'though greatly exhausted still showed a profit.' Quarries 20 feet square were let at 6d. a square foot and 10s. a year 'lord's rent'. Tile as well as freestone was taken, the tilers paying 1d. per hundredweight for their material. The whole was valued at £41. 10s. in 1776. By 1798 the quarry was 'already run over in such a manner that the workman scarcely know where to look for another.'

There is evidence that the quarries worked continuously into the 19th century, although the trade slumped badly in the 1830's. By 1838 there was only one quarry occupied by John Trask, tenant of Abbey Farm. But the trade revived and by 1861 there were four stonemasons resident in Ham-sub-Norton, and by 1863 six quarries were being worked, five belonging to the lord of the manor; three years later two more were opened and by 1875, 12 were in production. Eli Williams, tenant of one of the Phelips quarries in 1863, had himself become a quarry owner within 12 years. But again the trade declined at the end of the century so that four stonemasons were operating in 1897 and only two in 1902. In 1910 the surviving quarries were being worked by the Ham Hill and Doulting Stone Company which was in turn taken over by the United Stone Firms Limited before 1914. By 1919 a sole quarry owner survived, and the quarries were being effectively worked out. Under later ownership of The Bath and Portland Group, the quarries were worked sporadically as occasion demanded.

The villages that contained Gerard's little parishes had, of course, done more than provide stone during their two thousand years of history. In the hillside community were sheep and crop farmers, and craftsmen of many trades. Two mills on Stoke Manor were mentioned in the Domesday Survey, and survived through the ages as Petherton Bridge Mill, for the fulling of wool, and Stoke Mill for corn. (In 1809 there was trouble with the water supply when 'the mill next down the river' penned up the water, preventing the undershot wheel of Petherton Bridge Mill from working.)

The village of Ham held an annual fair, which had first been granted by the Earl of Mortain in 1118; early in the 17th century it was already held on St. Mark's Day, the 25th of April. In the late 18th century the fair was held around a Fairhouse where 'all sorts of cattle and pedlary were marketed,' but by 1775 'the tolls were scarcely worth collecting, largely because Mr. Phelips of Montecute was exercising great pains to encourage Montecute's fair on the same day.'

An attraction at Ham's Fair must have been the gloves made in the village of Stoke, which in the 18th century became one of the most important centres of the Somerset glove industry. In 1798 workers in the industry were housed in 'some very poor huts' on the waste of Ham Hill: the villagers tried to pull down the huts to frighten them away but the industry survived. By 1861 there were four factories and when in 1873 trade in gloves declined, Richard Southcombe introduced the manufacture of gaiters and spats. The firm he founded is one of four that remain today.

But today the hill where 'some buried Caesar bled' is silent of industry and calm in a new role. For recently this land was restored to the Duchy of Cornwall by the ceding of the leases held by the Phelips Trust and The Bath and Portland Group. Now it is a countryside park, notable for its magnificent prospect of five counties. Only the older inhabitants can remember the quarry in full activity, and they may also still ponder the secrets of Ham Hill when ghostly lights flickered once more up in the little parishes during the Second World War.

7

The Medieval Mason

THE ROMAN CLAUDIUS brought masonry to England in AD 43. Throughout the western Roman Empire, architecture and sculpture stemmed from Graeco-Roman beginnings. But there were older cililizations in which masonry had been practised and perfected; an early example was the Coptic art so well demonstrated in the pyramids of Egypt. The Egyptian demi-god Imhotep, who lived in the 3rd dynasty (circa 2980–2900 BC) was not only one of the earliest philosophers and wise men known to the world, but was also the ancestor of a long line of architects and master builders. The architecture of the Levant affected the later Gothic and Byzantine civilizations, and so brought its influence to Europe.

In England, the early Patent Rolls and Calendars of Close Rolls, now preserved in the Public Records Office in London, contain many references to masonry. They reveal that 'in every age Monarchs themselves have been promoters of the Art, and have not thought it derogatory to their dignity to exchange the sceptre for the trowel.' Indeed they joined in the mysteries of masonry and in assemblies of masons. King Athelstan (AD 924–940) was commended for his interest in the science of masonry, and the Old Charges speak of kings who loved masons well.

In western Europe the church of the Holy Roman Empire was the first significant patron of architecture and masonry. Among early references to the training of masons are those at Chartres made during the building of the transept porches of the Cathedral. Chartres, begun in 1194 but not completed until 1260, was the main training ground in Gothic art for the masons of the church, who went thence to build the cathedrals of Notre Dame, Amiens, and Reims. The work of maintaining cathedrals, as well as building them, has given the world its finest hereditary examples of Gothic architecture; maintenance required the setting up of masons' yards within cathedral precincts, and many of these yards still serve their purpose.

The church was not alone as a patron of the masons, for rulers had always needed castles. In England the interests of State and Church were brought together at an early date through the devotion of Edward the Confessor. Benedictine monks had built a primitive church on the site of the present Westminster Abbey when it was still an island in the River Thames, and Edward, inspired by the sanctity of the spot, re-built the monastery as the Church of St. Peter. So impressed was William the Conqueror with the devotion of Edward that he chose the church of St. Peter for his coronation, inaugurating a tradition that has lived to the present day. For his palace William built the Tower of London 'to whit the greate white and square tower there, about the year of Christ 1078.' He appointed Gundulph, then Bishop of Rochester, to be principal surveyor and overseer of that work. The building of the Tower was spread over many years, and the outer wall facing the ditch, the Traitors' Gate, and the Tower Wharf, were built by Adam of Lambourne in the reign of Henry III. It was Henry III who in 1245 demolished the whole of the east end of the Confessor's church at Westminster and began the building of the present Abbey church in its place.

Classically, masons only prepare work which can be set out and accomplished geometrically. At an early stage however there was a 'carver mason' whose work overlapped the simple beginnings of the world of sculpture, so that the field of masonry embraced all the stages from receiving dressed stone taken out of quarries to the embellishment of buildings with stone carving. In the thirteenth century tomb monuments were introduced as a development of masonry, the earliest including those of Henry II of England, his wife Eleanor of Aquitaine, and their 'knight-errant' son Richard I. The tomb monument had been a logical development from religious sculptures such as the great Tympanum of the Last Judgement on the façade of the thirteenth century Bourges

Cathedral. It was a short step from tomb monuments to effigies which commemorated people or occasions. Early examples of effigies are the Eleanor Crosses which mark the funeral route of Richard I's Queen Eleanor of Castile, from Lincoln to London. Master Alexander of Abingdon the Imager carved the Cross at Waltham, and also the original Cross at Charing Cross, removed by Order of Parliament in 1647 but reproduced there in the nineteenth century. The sculpting of the effigies on the tombs of Aveline and Crouchback dated 1296–1300, are also attributed to Alexander.

The building of Westminster Abbey became the special care of the English kings in which respect it differed from the great number of church buildings that were the care of bishops, abbots, and other church dignitaries. It is almost certain that Westminster Abbey was built to the design of Henry, the Master of the King's Masons who received the gift of a robe of office from Henry III on 10th December, 1243; the robe consisting of tunic and super-tunic. Henry became head of the architectural artists known as Master Masons to the King. From the similarities between the cathedral at Reims and Westminster Abbey, and from the fact that Master Henry's son Hugh described himself as 'Hugh, son of the late Master Henry der Reynes Mason', it is held by some that Master Henry may himself have come from Reims. It is more probable however that he was a Londoner with connections at Rayne, the Essex village just to the west of Braintree. The Abbey has the unusual distinction of maintaining one style throughout, although centuries elapsed between its foundation and completion.

Although Master Henry had made a careful study of the contemporary French cathedrals of Amiens and Reims and incorporated at Westminster such features as flying buttresses and rose windows, he was a brilliant architect in his own right and the result of his work has been described as 'a great French thought expressed in excellent English.' Henry was succeeded by John de Gloucester whose term of office as Master of the King's Masons lasted from 1253–1261. John was provided for life with two robes of good squirrel furs 'such as the knights of the household receive'; this did not gain him a suitable reward for his labour, however, for at his death he was in the King's debt for 80 marks, which his estate was unable to match.

Following John de Gloucester came Robert de Beverle who held office until 1284. Thereafter there is no record of King's Master Masons until 1336 when William de Rameseye was appointed by Edward III as Master Mason of the new Chapter House of St. Paul's Cathedral. William was also appointed chief surveyor to the Tower of London and other castles, for which he was to receive a robe and 12d. daily for wages. William de Rameseye was named representative of the Aldersgate Ward of the City of London in the first existing list of Common Councilmen of the City.

Masons were now divided into three classes—squarers of stone, setters of stone, and masons. The squarer of stone had to work without the advantages of modern equipment; to square a block, he first had to produce a flat side, which he did by 'boning'. Starting with points at two adjacent corners of the stone and using only hammer, chisel, and eye, he first cut a level edge. When he had levelled the four edges of the top face of the stone, the centre of this face was punched out, at all times using his eye to perfect a level surface. Once the first side was levelled, each of the four adjacent sides was cut at right angles in similar fashion, and the block was finally turned on to one side for the sixth side to be finished.

By the middle of the fourteenth century the practice of 'taking' workers for the King's service had been introduced, and this applied to many trades including masons. When Robert of Gloucester was named King's Mason by a patent of 1360, the printed Calendar read: 'appointment of the King's Mason Master Robert de Gloucestere to take masons for the King's works in the Castle of Windesore and put them to work there at the King's wages and to arrest masons found contrariant or rebellious and bringing them to the castle to be there imprisoned until they find security to stay in those works according to the injunction of the said Robert.' In the period 1358–1361 there were 23 patents as to taking masons for the Royal Works. In 1363 when William of Wykeham was in charge of the works at Windsor Castle a writ, in French, directed Thomas de Musgrave, Sheriff of York, to take 'vint & quatre masons' and to send them to Windsor Castle in March of that year. The Sheriff's expenses in 'divers liberties in his Bailywick' were disallowed but he was paid for 'thirty red caps' (rubeis capiciis) with other liveries of dyed ffustyan, bought for 30 masons chosen and taken in the aforesaid county and to be sent to the King's Castle of Windsor, lest they should escape from the custody of the conductor (ductoris).

There is little evidence for the Grant of Patents appointing King's Master Masons for areas north of the River Trent. Certainly in 1323, Nicholas de Derneford had been named as Master of Works at Beaumaris Castle and other castles in Wales; and John Rogers the King's Master Mason in the reign of Henry VIII was employed by the King in France and as far north as Berwick. Nevertheless there had been a sharp division between the masons north and south of the Trent, and when William of Colchester was sent to York by Henry V the masons there 'gave him a very warm but most unbrotherly reception'.

After Master Robert of Gloucester came Henry de Yevele (Yeovil) who in 1360 was appointed to be Disposer of the King's Works pertaining to the art of masonry in the Palace of Westminster and the Tower of London, 'taking in the office 12d. a day by the hands of the King's Clerk William de Lambhith, Surveyor of the Works.' In 1356 Henry de Yevele was chosen by his own trade-fellows as one of the most skilful men of the trade to represent them before the Mayor, Aldermen, and Sheriffs of the City of London. Henry was one of six 'mason hewers' and another six represented the light masons and setters. This body of masons negotiated with the City Corporation, producing regulations that were accepted for the trade, including the rule that no-one should set an apprentice to work except in the presence of his master. In 1369 Henry's appointment, which had been 'during the King's pleasure' was extended for the duration of his life, and he was granted a Winter Robe yearly 'of the suit of the Esquires of the Household, or an allowance in lieu thereof'. Within a matter of weeks Henry was authorized by the King to take masons and put them to work at the King's wages 'for such time as may be necessary and to commit to prison all contrariants and rebels to be detained until the King give other order touching their punishment'.

The early love of kings for masons had evaporated somewhat in the medieval years, and the mason enjoyed little more sympathy from the Corporation of the City of London. In the closing years of the 14th century the Corporation ordered that in each of the 24 wards of the City 'two good and honest men should be assigned to discover what masons or carpenters took wages contrary to the statute'. A proclamation of May 1382 stated 'the better sort of carpenter do not take between this and Michaelmus next for the working day when he works more than 8d. And the better sort of mason between this and the said feast for the working day more than 8d. And that on feast days when they do nothing they shall take no pay, but on Saturday if they work 2 hours afternoon they shall take pay for a whole day . . . And if anyone gives to carpenters, masons, or to their mates more or otherwise than is aforesaid he incurs the forfeiture of half a mark to the use of the Commonalty each time that he is convicted thereof. And if any carpenter, mason, tylere, daubere, take from anyone more or otherwise than is aforesaid he incurs the forfeiture of half a mark to the use of the Commonalty each time that he is convicted thereof'.

The masons of London first existed as a 'Company by Prescription', their trade regulations having been passed by the Court of Aldermen in 1356. The earliest notice of the masons as a City Guild or Fraternity occurs in Guildhall records for 1376, in the reign of Edward III. There the masons were included in a list of City Companies entitled to send representatives to Common Council, and the masons had four members. At this time the Company was sometimes referred to as the Company of Freemasons (similarly the Vintners were referred to as Freevintners), the masons being free of indentures and thus masters. The masons in Common Council were more concerned to regulate the trade than to protect the rights—if any—of the labouring mason; it was not until 75 years later that the principle of paying more money for a longer day's work in the summer was introduced: at Eton College, where 3/- per week or 6d. per day had been paid all the year round up to 1454, higher summer rates for Freemasons were introduced in 1456.

In 1472 the Masons received a grant of armorial bearings, an honour that implied the status of a corporate body in a position 'to sue and be sued'. The Company was granted its livery in 1481, and early in the 16th century the name changed from the Fellowship of Masons to the Company of Freemasons. At the threatened invasion of the Armada, the company bore its share of the cost of providing adequate defence by sea and land, and from records of expenditure under the Stuarts, the company like other city companies was subject to heavy taxation to provide corn and coal, and powder and shot, at a time when, according to Butler,

> 'Civil Dudgeon first grew high
> and men fell out they knew not why.'

By the time the Company became the Worshipful Company of Masons (by grant of Charter in 1677) the master masons had become a trade, with recognizable rules and regulations controlling their working conditions and procedures.

8

The Fated Cathedral

WHEN ETHELBERT, King of Kent, was converted to Christianity in the year 604, Mellitus, consecrated Bishop of London, set about the building of a church on the site of the present St. Paul's Cathedral. Little is known of this first building except that in 961 there was a fire followed by restoration, and in 1087 or 1088 there was a second fire which caused the structure to be rebuilt entirely. The second building was indeed a cathedral, and it was finally completed in about the year 1285, with 12 bays in its Norman nave and a choir in early English Gothic. The whole building was some 600 feet in length and the spire ranged to 493 feet, over 125 feet higher than the cross of the present St. Paul's Cathedral. This spire was struck by lightning in 1561; the building caught fire and the roof of the nave fell in. The burning of the roof caused the walls to spread so that they went 10 inches out of the perpendicular and were to remain so for just over 100 years. After the fire the cathedral had a stunted appearance, for the great spire was not re-built; and it was not until 1620, that Dr. King, Bishop of London, preaching before James I and the Lord Mayor of London inspired the appointment of a commission for the restoration of the cathedral.

His successor, Bishop Lord, carried on the restoration of old St. Paul's during the early part of King James I's reign, the work being superintended by Inigo Jones. The interior was finished, and at the west end there was erected Jones's stately portico, designed on the orders of Charles I and bearing the statues of James and Charles: it was carved in Portland stone. The cathedral was but a part of Inigo Jones's plan to use the stone of Portland to beautify London. It had been Inigo Jones who in the second quarter of the 17th century re-opened the neglected quarries at Portland and brought Portland stone to popularity.

When Peter Mundy, a Cornishman, visited the Island of Portland in July 1635 in the course of his travels across Europe and Asia, he described the scene at the quarries: 'I went to the hewers of stone, which was quarried for the reparation of St. Paules Church in London. There were about 200 hundred workemen some hewing out of the cliffe alofte, some squareing, some caryeing down, others ladeinge. Some stones there were ready squared and formed of nine, ten and eleven tonnes weight, as they said. Some of them were ready squared alofte and sent downe in carts made for the purpose.'

Inigo Jones is ranked among the most important of the great English architects. His early life was given to the design of theatrical settings, where he introduced the proscenium arch and the concept of movable scenery. He only turned to architecture when he was appointed Royal Surveyor in 1615, at the age of 42. He then went on to design the Queen's house at Greenwich for Anne of Denmark and, in the next six years, to transform Westminster. It has been said that Whitehall was virtually a thoroughfare of Portland stone: the Banqueting Hall there is not only a beautiful building but is perhaps also the supreme example of what Portland stone is and can be (see Plate 11). In addition there remain today the German Chapel Royal built for Charles I's queen and known as Marlborough House Chapel, and the gateway of Ashburnham House, now part of Westminster School. Apart from this and the work Inigo Jones did for the tottering St. Paul's Cathedral (it had been in a state of dangerous disrepair even before his birth), he virtually introduced the concept of town planning to England with the layout of Covent Garden and Lincoln's Inn Fields. He had travelled through Italy, Germany and France in his early thirties, and undoubtedly this gave him the inspiration to develop his exquisite taste in Renaissance architecture, and to use his skill to raise the poor standard of earlier British architecture.

But for all his brilliance Inigo Jones was treated more as a 'surveyor of works' than as an architect, for this was the custom of the time. It was Jones's misfortune that he was a devoted royalist and thus became an object of suspicion when the Parliamentarians began their attack on the throne. He lived to see St. Paul's Cathedral desecrated and ruined; and following the Battle of Worcester he saw his lovely portico in St. Paul's filled with stalls and booths and used as a market place. In 1652 Inigo Jones died in the shadow of the cathedral, poor and lonely. Christopher Wren was then 20 years old.

Wren came from a distinguished ecclesiastical family; he was the son of a Wiltshire clergyman who became Dean of Windsor, and his uncle was Bishop of Ely. Christopher was educated at Westminster School where he showed early signs of inventive ability, and went on to Wadham College where he was much influenced by the scientists intruded into Oxford, the home of Classicism, by the action of the Commonwealth government. Wren, already regarded as a scientific prodigy, was soon elected a Fellow of All Souls. Here, the parallel between Christopher Wren and Leonardo da Vinci is too close to be ignored. Da Vinci was a student of all the natural sciences; his tireless curiosity led him into mathematics, astrology, architecture, town planning, mechanics, and anatomy, in addition to the broad range of his genius in painting and drawing. Wren, some two hundred years later, was to excel in all these sciences and skills except painting; he was at the very centre of the movement that classified observations and hypotheses and transformed them into sciences.

Towards the end of the Commonwealth Wren became Professor of Mathematics at Gresham College London from which he resigned in 1660 to take up the Savilian Professorship of Astronomy at Oxford; in 1662 he was a joint founder of the Royal Society (which Wren had earlier discussed with John Wilkins and a group of thinkers at Wadham College) and Wren became its President in 1681–83. The only early indication that he might turn to architecture was in his considerable talent for drawing, particularly in his anatomical studies. Wren's first architectural works included the building of the beautiful chapel at Pembroke Hall Cambridge at a time when his uncle was Bishop of Ely; this may account for the fact that the chapel was built in classical style. It is perhaps typical of Wren's approach that when another of his first important commissions, the building of the Sheldonian Theatre at

Oxford was conceived on the drawing board, it incorporated a flat roof which from a theoretical point of view had occupied Wren's mind for some years. Before the Sheldonian was completed Wren had been retained to consider the restoration of old St. Paul's Cathedral which was now suffering additional neglect from 20 years of misuse since the outbreak of the Civil War. Wren and John Evelyn were appointed to a new Commission to study the old Cathedral's needs. Charles II was influenced by Evelyn to appoint Wren as assistant to Sir John Denham, the Surveyor General of Works, and thus Wren's architectural career started in earnest.

When a year or two later the City of London was devastated by the Great Fire, Wren was further commissioned to consider and advise on the re-planning of the whole City and this is perhaps a more important aspect of Wren's work even than the design and building of the new cathedral. Wren had taken the opportunity to visit Paris in 1665 where he concedes in his own hand that 'his interests were even more architectural than scientific'. In 1669 as a result of much jobbery Wren was appointed Surveyor of the Royal Works, and this had a remarkable consequence in which perhaps there was some poetic justice. For achieving this appointment over the heads of John Webb and Hugh May, two men of considerable architectural experience, Wren was committed solely to ecclesiastical building, while Webb and May were commissioned for important non-ecclesiastical buildings undertaken for the Crown.

The disastrous state of old St. Paul's after the Commonwealth, is told dramatically in a letter sent by W. Sancroft Dean of St. Paul's to Christopher Wren at Oxford. Sancroft wrote:

'What you whispered in my ear, at your last coming hither, is now come to pass. Our work at the west end of St. Paul's is falling about our ears. Your quick eye discerned the walls and pillars "gone off from the perpendiculars" and I believe other effects too, which are now exposed to every common observer.

About a week since (we being at work about the third pillar from the west end on the south side, which we had new cased with stone where it was most defective almost up to the

chapter) a great weight fallen from the high wall so disabled
the vaulting of the side aisle by it, that it threatened a sudden
ruin so visibly that the workmen presently removed, and the
next night the whole pillar fell and carried scaffolds and all to
the very ground.'

The letter continues to comment on two defects in Inigo Jones's
work: first that his new case of stone in the upper walls though
massive was not set upon the upright of the pillars but upon the
core of the groins of the vaulting; and the other that there were no
keystones at all to tie the new work to the old.

'All this', said Sancroft
'being very heavy with the Roman ornaments on the top of
it, and being already so far gone outwards, cannot possibly
stand long. It is therefore the opinion of all men that we
proceed no farther at the west end. What we are to do next is
the present deliberation in which you are so absolutely and
indispensibly necessary to us that we can do nothing, resolve
on nothing, without you.
You will think fit I know to bring with you those excellent
drafts and designs you formerly favoured us with, and in the
meantime, till we enjoy you here, consider what to advise
that may be for the satisfaction of His Majesty and the whole
nation, an obligation so great and public that it must be
acknowledged by better hands than those of your affectionate
friend and servant, W. Sancroft.'

When Wren reported on the condition of the cathedral he said
'what time and weather has left entire, the calamity of the fire has
so weakened and so defaced that it now appears as some antique
ruin of 2000 years continuance'. He said that to repair it sufficiently would be like the mending of the Argo-Nairs—a reference
to the frequent repairs to the Argo which left 'scarce anything of
the old'. The restoration of the old cathedral, Wren concluded,
was past remedy. Denham himself was 'an indifferent architect if
one at all' and the responsibility for the new St. Paul's was to fall
entirely upon Wren. Later the committee resolved to instruct
Wren 'to frame a design handsome and noble built, suitable to all
the ends of it, and the reputation of the City and the nation; to take
for granted that money will be had to accomplish it or, however,

to let it lie by, till we have before us a prospect of so much as may reasonably encourage us to begin.' This gave Wren what was perhaps the greatest opportunity of his life and he selected the oolite of Portland as his material for transforming his dream into reality. From now on Wren was preoccupied with his new Cathedral and the City churches, and this increasing pressure of work caused him to resign in 1673 from his Professorship of Astronomy at Oxford.

Before the new cathedral could arise the old cathedral had to be demolished. Apart from the damage caused by the Parliamentarians, the stress of the roof was in any event too heavy for the pillars of the nave. Each pillar, though 11 feet in diameter, was only cased in stone but filled with rubble. The roof was cracked and ready to fall in and the tower which was leaning dangerously was supported with buttresses. Of Inigo Jones' Portico it was said that it had been 'nearly deprived of the excellent beauty and strength which time alone and weather could have no more overthrown than the natural rocks, so great and good were the materials and so skilfully were they laid after a true Roman manner. But so impatient is Portland stone of fire that many tons are scaled off and the columns flawed quite through.'

By 1673 Wren was ready to level the walls of the old cathedral to the ground and as demolition began the best building stone and other materials were sold 'only for re-building parish churches and for no other use whatsoever'. But the exception, Kentish ragstone, which had been used in the old cathedral as rubble, was sold to the authorities for the metalling of roads.

King Charles II issued an order in council for taking down the walls of the east end, the old choir, and the tower 'for clearing the ground in order to lay a fresh foundation'. Wren planned this demolition by instructing the surveyor to place scaffolds high enough to extend over heaps of rubble that already lay in the way in order to get close to the remaining stand of the cathedral; thus gaining more room every day he came to the middle tower which bore the 200 feet high remains of the steeple. At this point the labourers refused to work beneath the steeple and Wren concluded to facilitate the work by using gunpowder. A hole about four feet in width was dug by the side of the northwest pillar of the tower; it was one of four pillars each 14 feet in diameter. When the labourers had dug to the foundation with tools made for the purpose and wrought a hole two feet square level with the centre of the pillar, Wren placed there a little deal box containing 18 lbs of powder. A cane was fixed to the box with a quick match within it which reached from the box to the ground above, and along the ground was laid a train of gunpowder. After the mine had been carefully closed up with stone and mortar to the top of the ground, Wren observed the effect of the blow.

'The powder not only lifted up the whole angle of the tower with two great arches that rested upon it but also two adjoining arches of the aisles and all above them and this it seemed to do somewhat leisurely, cracking the walls to the top, lifting visibly the whole weight by nine inches which suddenly jumping down, made a great heap of ruin in the place without scattering. It was half a minute before the heap already fallen opened in two or three places and emitted some smoke.'

At this point in the demolition, Wren was called away to Portland and the management of a second mine was left to a subordinate who, 'too wise in his own conceit, put in a greater quantity of gunpowder and according to the chroniclers' complaint, neither went low enough nor sufficiently fortified the mouth of the mine.' Though the explosion was successful, one stone was shot out to the opposite side of the churchyard through an open window into the room of a private house where women were sitting at work. Though no-one was injured the neighbours were so alarmed that they petitioned the builders not to explode mines below their windows. So the clerk in charge fixed up a battering ram made from a strong mast 40 foot long, on the bigger end of which an iron spike was fixed. Suspending this from a massive tripod, 30 men, 15 aside, vibrated the battering ram against the wall for the whole day with little apparent success. Inspired by hope of double pay the workmen returned to the attack on the second day, when the wall 'trembled at the top and in a few hours fell'. All the remaining walls of the old cathedral were levelled in this way.

9

Resurgam

To pay for restoring the City of London and raising the new Cathedral after the Great Fire, a tax was imposed in June 1667 on every chaldron of coal imported into the City. No less than 4,696,998 chaldrons of coal were imported into the City during the 17 years for which this tax lasted, but the Cathedral was not the chief beneficiary. The coal tax was divided as to 3s. per chaldron to the City, one shilling and a penny half-penny to pay for building other churches and only four-and-a-half pence to St. Paul's Cathedral. This realised for the building of St. Paul's Cathedral a fund of £88,064 and for the parish churches of the City £264,206. Under the Acts which raised this coal tax dating from James II onwards, there was also a borrowing clause, under which large sums were borrowed, incurring interest of over £11,000.

A minute of the Committee of St. Paul's Cathedral to Thomas Gilbert, overseer of His Majesty's quarries at Portland instructed Gilbert to quarry such stone as may be required for the erection of the Cathedral (see Fig. 2 page 225). A text of an Order in Council of Charles II laid down that Portland stone should only be exported from the Isle of Portland 'on the signature of Doctor Christopher Wren, Surveyor of Our Works.' Wren must have given careful thought to the choice of stone for building the new cathedral. The Norman Conquest had brought the use of Norman stone from Caen where the French oolite originates and corresponds rather to Bath than to Portland stone. The Caen stone put into Winchester Cathedral showed signs of failure after only 60 years and in the case of Canterbury Cathedral the constant need for renovation has always been well known. It would seem that though Portland badly needed London as a showcase the City needed Portland even more. The City was to use six million tons of the Island stone.

The effect on the Island of Portland of the building of St. Paul's Cathedral was considerable, but by an Act of God a great landslide had occurred on the east side of the Island in or around the year 1636. A whole expanse of cliff tumbled outward to the sea exposing literally hundreds of thousands of tons of stone which was readily workable by the quarrymen of those days using the primitive tools at their disposal (see Fig. 3 page 224). Most of the quarrying was confined to the cliff edges where time and weather had exposed the stone and made it more readily accessible. The stone was quarried and dressed in Portland, but masonry was an itinerant craft and the stone masons would have journeyed to London to fashion the stone.

The rough blocks of stone were prepared under the superintendence of Wren's surveyor Thomas Gilbert, using a kivel or hammer six to eight pounds in weight and even up to 16 pounds in weight, for the purpose of dressing or 'knocking off the rough'. Thomas Gilbert was a member of the London Masons' Company and his family continued in the stone trade in Portland at least for another 100 years. Gilbert was responsible for constructing roads and piers on the Island to handle the St. Paul's stone. In 1696 and '97, £520 was spent in this way and in 1698, another £580 was expended because of 'ye sliding of ye ground into the sea whereby the former way and pier were ruined'. (See Fig. 4 page 226.)

The quarries at Portland are layered with a mould and clay debris with 'slatey beds, dirt beds, and fossil trays at the top.' Below come the topcap, skullcap, and true roach; the true roach is always incorporated with the whitbed off which it has to be split. Below the whitbed comes the curf-flinty, a very white stone not capable of weathering; and then the base bed roach (much used in modern architecture because of the pattern of its high fossil content); succeeded by the base bed itself. This is the finest of all the beds but does not weather well and is much used for engineering works. The whitbed, though little inferior to it is the best general building stone. At the bottom of all come the flat or flint beds. To work the quarry the upper strata were blasted and the lower beds quarried by means of wedges and levers.

The quarried block was brought to London in Thames barges which picked up their cargoes at the piers known as King's Pier, Folley Pier, Flews Pier, and Durdle Pier of which remains can still be seen today. The islanders constructed these piers on either side of the Island so that loading was always possible at one side or the other opposite to the prevailing wind. The loading was carried out by the use of jacks which relied upon manpower; there was no steam or electricity and often there were no winches. It was a hard job, and Wren himself was a hard task master. He insisted on the stone for St. Paul's lying on the sea beach for three years before permitting its shipment. The stone was conveyed on sledges to the stone piers where it was loaded into flat-bottomed boats and thence to the barge in the offing. The ship's tackle would then be the only means available to lift the large stones but it was done; and thousands of tons were thus conveyed each year for the sites in London.

In the last quarter of the 17th century 50 churches were being constructed in London and most were being faced with Portland stone. Wren was always hungry for stone, and when adequate supplies did not reach him from Portland he had to turn elsewhere. He incorporated more of the Caen stone from old St. Paul's than he would have wished. Some of the Caen stone got into the construction of the drum of the dome where it can be identified by its Norman chiselling; but unable to stand the pressure, it has been crushed. Wren had hoped that the Caen stone 'more beautiful than durable' if not exposed to the air and to the smoke of sea-coal would not deteriorate, but the London atmosphere has in fact reached and attacked it, even in its hidden recesses. About two-thirds of the stone used in the building of St. Paul's was Portland stone and the other stones used included Burford, Headington (Oxfordshire), Beer, Caen, Reigate, Ketton, Tadcaster, and Guildford. Of all these other stones some 26,000 tons were used, compared with over 50,000 tons from Portland. Up to Michaelmas, 1700, 50,322 tons of Portland stone had been billed for a total of £28,065. 16s. 7¾d, plus freight of £28,951.2s.8d. The dome was to use 10,000 tons more. Small amounts of marbles for specific purposes were also incorporated into the cathedral. Grinling Gibbons' bill for stone carving was £1919 while his woodcarvings in the choir cost another £1660.

It is generally acknowledged that Portland stone weathers better than any other limestone and in its structure and formation the oolites (egg or roe stones) are 'akin to coral—organic and aqueous'. Well-weathered Portland show a similarity of textures to the weathered surfaces of marbles from the Purbeck Beds. It was not possible for Wren to have divined the peculiar phenomenon of weathering of Portland stone that was noted by observers in later years. The stone spires of Wren's city churches became leached and shining above the great mass of blackened wall face below, the homely gift of London's smoke. In this Wren would have seen a shining example of da Vinci's studies in light and shade. This effect is now being lost as buildings are being cleaned and soot pollution lessened by the compulsory introduction of smokeless fuels.

Wren had made a number of designs for St. Paul's and in 1673 a patent was issued under the Great Seal of England for the erection of the new Cathedral. On 20th November of that year, Christopher Wren was knighted. When in the next year Charles II at last gave his approval, the Royal Warrant Design as presented and passed did not satisfy Wren nor represent his concept of the kind of building that should be erected. Liberty was given to Wren to make some variations 'rather ornamental than essential as from time to time he should see proper' and the whole work was left to his management. Wren was of course fighting to a certain extent with himself and his first and even his final conceptions failed to satisfy him completely. But with a design accepted and funds provided Wren went about the appointment of his foreman and staff to build the cathedral. It is recorded that Wren undoubtedly disobeyed the King's orders, for essential rather than ornamental alterations were made in working out the plan of the St. Paul's Cathedral we know today. Objections were not raised however for by this time Wren stood pre-eminent among architects and his reputation restrained the comments of those in authority.

When Wren had been bringing down the old cathedral he found by digging pits that the earlier cathedral rested on a layer of very close and hard pot-earth—the sort of clay which potters use. This varied in thickness from six foot on the north side of the churchyard to four foot on the south side and Wren concluded 'that the same ground which had borne so weighty a building might reasonably be trusted again'. Wren did not build on the old foundations however, but 'laid the middle line more declining to the north east than it was before'. Proceeding from the west end through the dome to the east end he found no difficulty until at the extreme north east corner 'he fell, in prosecuting the design, upon a pit where all the pot-earth had been robbed by the potters of old time. It was no little perplexity', it was written, 'to fall into this pit at last'.

Wren knew very well that under the layer of pot-earth there was no good ground to be found till he came to the low water mark of the Thames at least 40 feet beneath. He rejected a proposal to sink piles and, 'wishing to build for eternity' is said to have sunk a pit 18 foot square to the sea beach in which he built a solid pier of masonry until within 15 feet of ground level, from which point he turned an arch to the foundations where they were broken off. When excavating for the new cathedral, graves of Norman and Saxon origin were discovered together with Roman urns. There were theories that a Temple of Diana had existed on the site of St. Paul's and a Temple of Apollo on the site of Westminster Abbey, but Wren believed in neither and he certainly discovered no evidence of any earlier foundations.

There are many drawings for St. Paul's Cathedral and none of them agree with the building as it was finished; to this extent therefore there must be some mystery as to the precise detail of Wren's foundations. The concept which was common to all Wren's drawings however was that of the dome, varied from time to time in outline and altitude, but always the dominant feature. It is thought that the dome of St. Peter's in Rome gave him this idea, but it is possible also that Christopher Wren the astrologer had some thought of the cupolas housing the telescopes of the Royal Observatory at Greenwich which he had designed and built in 1675 some 35 years before the new St. Paul's was finished. After Wren had formed the foundations of St. Paul's and the preliminary work was completed, a grand masonic ceremony took place. In 1673 the King, with Grand Master Rivers, his architects and craftsmen, nobility and gentry, the Lord Mayor and Aldermen, and Bishops and Clergy, in due course levelled the footstone of the new St. Paul's designed by Deputy Grand Master Wren, in a ceremony 'by him conducted as Master of the Works and Surveyor, with his wardens Edward Strong, senior and junior.'

Christopher Wren had received his appointment as architect for St. Paul's Cathedral at a yearly salary of £200, which for his masterly skills would seem to compare unfavourably with the £100 a year paid to his labourers. Presumably John Oliver, his assistant surveyor who directed the workmen, measured the mason's work and bought the materials, and Laurence Spenser, Clerk of the Works who overlooked the men, would have been paid something between the two figures. An individual called 'Clerk of the Cheque' corresponding to the modern time-keeper called over the labourers three times a day. These with Thomas Strong, a Master Mason, and Richard Jennings, a master carpenter, were all devoted to Wren and served him faithfully. On 21st June 1675 the first stone of St. Paul's was laid by Christopher Wren and his master mason, 'no King, Bishop, Dean or Lord Mayor' being present.

To ascend St. Paul's, Wren was hauled up in a basket: a dangerous method yet the only one that was known for examining work in progress at high levels at that time. Nine labourers were killed in the course of building the cathedral, which in view of the magnitude and duration of the task was not a great number. A labourer called Throwgood and Thomas Piggott were killed by a fall from the high tower, and Will Hibworth by a fall from the east end; the compensation given was hardly excessive being only £4. 17s. 6d. for the three. John Capon, a labourer, fell from the top of the old west gable end and Patrick Pratt fell in the church; and the cause of the deaths of Will Banks and Ted Walter is not stated. Representatives of these four received in the aggregate £10. 10s. 6d.—described at the time as 'a miserly benevolence which contrasts unpleasantly with the amount of gratuities to minor legal and city officials.' As yet, it has been said, the Employers' Liability Act and the Illicit Commissions Act were still 'in the womb of the future'.

An examination of incidental expenses in building the cathedral reflects a state of dishonesty no better, perhaps, than that of the present day. Actual cash losses included £405 in 'guinys', £5. 4s. in broad pieces, £1. 13s. 9d. in Louis d'Or's, £40 in hammered silver and £120 14s. 7d. in hand-written bank bills. There is also evidence of shady transactions and illicit commissions, as for example fees to keepers for presents of venison, and a payment of £50 to a lawyer, Mr. Middleton, 'for a gratuity to silence his further craving'. Another entry refers to a gratuity to 'a person for service in obtaining ye impropriacon grant £50, where anonimity suggests something beyond modesty'.

Yet another example of the commercial morality of the day is disclosed in a note from Bridge and others, 'pretending several frauds to be practised in coal importation, and that they could prevent the same if they had encouragement'. Bridge negotiated an allowance of one sixth part of the produce of the duty over and above a total of £40,600 per annum at the rate of 3s. per chaldron and he contracted accordingly with the City of London and the Church Commissioners for their respective proportions of the said allowance 'which agreement though unwarrantable yet succeeded, and by this spoilation by Bridge and his partners some £786 was paid over to them before it was stopped'. The said Mr. Middleton received substantial sums as salary and also for legal charges concerning Bridge and Partners.

Wren worked very closely with his labourers during the building of the cathedral and it was noted by him that the men were given to swearing. Wren issued an order which was affixed in many parts of St. Paul's as building went on. It read:

'Whereas among labourers etc that ungodly custom of swearing is too frequently heard, to the dishonour of God and contempt of authority; and to the end therefore that such impiety may be utterly banished from these works, intended for the service of God and the honour of religion, it is ordered that customary swearing shall be a sufficient sign to dismiss any labourer that comes to the call. Clerk of Works upon sufficient proof shall dismiss them accordingly (and) if any master working task shall not upon admonition reform this profanation among his apprentices, servants and labourers, it shall be construed his fault and he shall be liable to be censured by the commissioner'.

These were among the troubles Wren faced as the building of the cathedral proceeded slowly. Parliament seized part of the fabric money and applied it to the expenses of King William's wars, so that Sir Christopher Wren complained that 'his wings had been clipped'. Another problem facing Wren was the quality of bricks which were then being manufactured. 'In the mighty demand for the hasty works', said Wren, 'the firebricks are being badly mixed and hastily burnt till they would hardly bear any weight upon them'. While acknowledging that Portland stone was best, Wren constantly complained of its cost and said it was not without its faults, referring no doubt to stone from the inferior beds which were used in the less important features of the cathedral.

On one occasion as the mighty structure rose, Wren was watching activities with some of his associates and called to one of the workmen to bring him a stone to mark a special spot. Wren noticed that the stone brought to him had an inscription upon it—the single word 'Resurgam'. This was regarded by Wren as a singularly happy omen. The stone was reckoned to have been part of the gravestone of Dr. John King, the Bishop of London who had preached in the old cathedral before King James I and his court in an appeal for its restoration. Wren delighted in this anecdote, and repeated it many times in his later life.

Eventually the time came for the great dome to be built, in itself a massive project. The inner dome is built of brick, plastered, and painted by Sir James Thornhill. From the floor of the interior of the cathedral to the open eye at the top of the dome is 218 feet. Over this inner dome is a cone 18 inches thick rising to support the Portland stone lantern which itself weighs 700 tons. The weight of the inner dome, the cone, and the outer dome are not known, but the aggregate must be enormous. This mass supported by eight piers had already sunk a few inches before the building was completed and since the principle of building on a flat table of reinforced concrete was unknown in Wren's day, this left the foundations of the individual piers to settle unequally.

Thus from the very beginning, the safety of the cathedral rested on the maintenance of subsoil consistency. The dome had settled even before the side walls of the cathedral were finished and this can be seen not only from the distortion of the windows and the inclination of horizontal mouldings but also from the diminishing courses of masonry which Wren had to use to bring the level of the parapet into true. Edward Strong was employed to make good some blemishes in the piers and arches caused by the unequal settlement, and 40 tons of Portland stone were employed to repair the south-eastern pier alone during the construction of the cathedral. Wren obviously mistrusted the supporting power of the soil on the eastern side of the cathedral where he had excavated to some 18 to 25 feet with a great spread of footings there—two or three times greater than he employed in other parts of the foundations.

Wren had noted that 'among all the compostures of the ancients, we find no cupolas raised above the necessary loading of the hemisphere', as in the case of the Pantheon and Sancta Sophia. Furthermore the general fashion in the Stuart epoch was for tall steeples, and in deference to this, Wren concluded that his cupola should be raised to a remarkable altitude. But Wren had posed for himself a mathematical and engineering problem which perhaps he alone in his age was able to resolve. He devised a dome of an unusual type, poising and counter-poising his weights and thrusts till he achieved one of the greatest marvels of building construction. With his master mason, Wren himself fixed the last stone to the cupola; and it was his son Christopher who in the presence of Mr. Strong and 'other free accepted masons chiefly employed in the execution of the work', laid the last stone on the top of the lantern. The exterior of the cathedral was completed and the scaffolding removed in 1710 (see Plates 11, 12 and 13).

When the opening ceremony was publicly announced, all London poured forth to witness the spectacle and it is said that 300,000 people thronged the metropolis. Henry Hart Milman who was Dean of St. Paul's in the middle 19th century conjured up the scene in these words: 'Picture the man at that hour actually at that giddy height looking up and around on this great matchless building: a creation of his own mind, the achievement of his sole care and skill, the whole building stretching out in all its perfect unison, its towers, its unrivalled dome, its crowning lantern and cross.'

London looked up in awe at the man who had become a legend in his own lifetime. From that great height, Wren could look down on the steeples of St. Mary Le Bow, St. Brides, St. Stephen's Wallbrook, and many others of his making; and in the distance he could see Greenwich Hospital, which was also being erected in Portland stone, webbed in scaffolding. In that moment of contemplation and satisfaction Wren must have thought his modest salary of £16. 13s. 4d. per month left him owing little to the world; and indeed, since the Act of Parliament defining his fees resolved that a moiety of them should be withheld 'towards the close of his labours', which resolve the committee actually put into effect, he may well have supposed that 'building for eternity' was very much a labour of love. To cap it all, Christopher Wren was accused of delaying the completion of the cathedral in order to sustain his modest salary, and in the 49th year of his holding office he was dismissed as Surveyor of Public Works. *Sic transit gloria mundi!*

Wren was too old to attend the dedication of the cathedral but in the last years of his life he was in the habit of being driven to London once a year to sit for a while under the dome of his Cathedral. During one of these journeys he caught a chill and died soon afterwards on the 25th February 1723 at the age of 91. He was buried in the crypt, and there the chapel was dedicated in his honour. His epitaph is fittingly worded '*Lector, si monumentum requiris, circumspice*'—'Reader, if you seek his monument, look around you.' (During the 500th anniversary of the Worshipful Company of Masons in 1972 a memorial to the masons who built the Cathedral, especially Edward and Thomas Strong, was put up directly below Wren's. It says 'remember the men who made shapely the stones of St. Paul's Cathedral'.) By the time Wren died he had laid down three principles to which building in England began to conform: they were 'beauty, firmness, and convenience.'

Wren's output had been prolific. While managing the cathedral enterprise, he had been following every step in the re-building of the City of London: he made certain that the streets were thrown open and churches were placed in commanding positions. He insisted upon stone or brick buildings and paved streets, and so intent was he for the future that where he found shabby and dangerous buildings being erected he petitioned the King to put a stop to this growing practice and the King in council invariably supported him.

Within the City's square mile Wren had been at work designing and supervising the building of the many City Churches. The money appropriated for these churches from the Coal Tax went in the first instance to building the bodies of the churches, and many of the towers were added later. It was the bodies of the churches therefore that represent Wren's earlier architectural style, reflecting his visits to Paris. This influence was later reinforced by the availability of French architectural engravings, especially those of the Invalides which were published in the course of the 1680's. In Wren's later work some influence of the Roman Baroque school can also be seen, possibly resulting from the increased availability of intaglios of Roman churches in the 1680's and 1690's. The School of Wren was supplanted by so called Palladianism of the Burlington and Kent group in the 1730's; the palladian theme, which had influenced Inigo Jones, was to be central to the work of John Wood, just starting at Bath.

The beautiful St. Mary le Bow in Cheapside was built in 1671: it was discovered that the original church had been built on the foundation of a Roman temple; the new church was one of Wren's finest. St. Mary at Hill was built in the following year and here Wren introduced the dome roof; this was again used in the church of St. Stephen, Walbrook (see Plate 14). St. Stephen's is a perfect example of Wren's work, and it is sad that in 1979 the church is in considerable danger from subsidence for the same reasons that could so well have affected St. Paul's.

In 1675 the church of St. Stephen's, Coleman Street was built and also St. Mildred's Poultry, a church that was doomed to be pulled down again in 1872; its stone was saved from the fate of being converted into cement by one Mr. Wright. He had it conveyed by water to St. Catherine Garth near the east coast of Lincoln to be built into a chapel. St. Brides Fleet Street was begun in 1675 but its wedding cake spire was not completed until 20 years later. The lovely St. Laurence Jewry standing by Guildhall, contains some of Grinling Gibbons' somewhat rare carvings in stone; they are of fruit subjects (see Plate 15). The inside of St. Mary's Abchurch built in 1686 is another of Wren's masterpieces. St. Andrew by the Wardrobe at Blackfriars was finished in red brick with stone dressing and then came St. Dunstan's in the East, built in 1689, the last of the churches that Wren completed. St. Dunstans has a curious spire resting on four arches springing from the angles of the tower.

Prior to the laying of the foundation of St. Paul's Wren had already used Portland stone for the Temple Bar and for the Monument erected in memory of the Great Fire of 1665, an occurrence Londoners were unlikely to forget (see Plate 16). When Wren carried out repairs to the White Tower (see Plate 17), one of the oldest parts of the Tower of London, his workmen came upon a wooden chest which proved to contain the remains of two children corresponding in age to the Princes Edward and Richard, murdered in 1573. The discovery was made while stones were being removed in the passage leading from the Royal lodgings to St. John's Chapel. By an order of Charles II the remains were re-interred in the Henry VII Chapel of Westminster Abbey.

Outside the City Wren had also been busy. Bishop Ward of Salisbury sought his advice and assistance in consequence of depredations to the cathedral at Salisbury during the Civil War. Wren found the tower to be out of plumb and 'took steps to prevent further mischief'. In 1674 Drury Lane Theatre was re-built to Wren's design; and in the following year the Observatory at Greenwich was completed. In the late 1670's the Chapel of Emmanuel College and the library of Trinity College, (see Plate 18) were erected at Cambridge, and at Oxford the Ashmolean Museum was built partly of Portland stone (see Plate 18). Wren also worked on Greenwich Palace, which he induced Charles II's Queen to convert into a seaman's hospital. Wren designed a number of the great town houses in Portland stone including Chesterfield, Uxbridge and Lansdowne. Later he designed Carlton House, of which the screen was subsequently removed to Buckingham Palace and the portico to the National Gallery. In the 1680's Wren continued with Chelsea Hospital and did much work at Hampton Court and Kensington Palace. In the year 1699 Wren turned his attention to Westminster Abbey and the great north window was re-built in Portland stone. Nine years later he built and completed the north front of the Abbey (see Plate 19); the western front was only restored by him.

During the 1690's Wren worked closely at the Office of Works with Nicholas Hawkesmore or Hawksmoor, Sir John Vanburgh and later with John James of Greenwich, and in his old age Wren was called to advise the church commissioners on the building of new churches in the London suburbs under an Act of Parliament of 1711. How Wren also managed to serve two terms in Parliament is beyond comprehension. He represented Plympton St. Maurice from 1685–87 and Weymouth from 1701–02.

From the day that Christopher Wren decided that the weight of St. Paul's Cathedral could be sustained by whatever combination of soils lay beneath it, the Cathedral has been at risk. It has been clearly established that, because the piers have independent foundations, any alteration to the consistency of the subsoil would cause these piers to settle unequally, those to the south probably spreading towards the declining hill with fatal results to the superstructure. It remained for history to show what could happen if solid heavy buildings were undermined. Charing Cross Station was to collapse, and Holy Trinity Church, Kingsway, which was a perfectly safe building in precisely the same way as St. Paul's today is safe, had to be demolished because of the building of the tram subway under Kingsway itself. The tram subway was at a depth of 24 feet from the road level, about 10 feet below the Holy Trinity foundations, and this resulted in fractures to the walls of the church extending to no less than 90 feet in length.

As London has developed the keepers of St. Paul's have had the responsibility to see that no such schemes were allowed to put the Cathedral in peril. As far back as 1831 Cockerell, then Surveyor of the Fabric, with George Rennie, the famous engineer, and Robert Smirke, the architect to the Cathedral, had protested in a joint report against the construction of a sewer on the south side of the Cathedral and running parallel with it; fortunately the views expressed by those experts were accepted. Then in 1890 the question of the Cathedral's safety was raised when the Central London Railway Bill was being promoted. Again in 1901 there was a proposal to construct a tube railway at Ludgate Hill and Carter Lane but it was abandoned in good time. Next came a suggestion to run a great east to west sewer passing so near the Cathedral as to give rise to anxiety.

An even more serious threat came when a project was mooted for a tram subway which was to run north and south under the east side of St. Paul's Churchyard. In 1910, London County Council applied to Parliament for power to run this tramway over the new St. Paul's Bridge (now Blackfriars Bridge) and to construct tram subways under Cannon Street to Cheapside at the eastern end of the Cathedral. It was realised that sinking these tunnels would drain the water from the subsoil of the Cathedral; the experts had always said this would inevitably affect the foundations which are exceedingly shallow for the size of the building.

Canon Alexander pointed out that St. Paul's was unquestionably the heaviest building in London 'with wide untied spaces and thus having to depend for stability on the immobility of its foundations.' Comment was made on vibration from motor omnibuses, for even then vibration was clearly felt in the Cathedral library from buses running along the eastern side of St. Paul's. 'This being the result of the passage of a three-and-a-half ton omnibus with rubber tyred wheels,' it was asked, 'what would be the effect of a much heavier vehicle with iron wheels running on iron rails at or below the level of the Cathedral foundations?'

The example of Holy Trinity Church, Kingsway was quoted pointing out that the conditions applying to the Kingsway tramway would apply equally to the new project: the subway would come within 70 feet of the structure itself and the excavations would be just seven feet below the level of the Cathedral foundations. Mr. Mervyn Macartney, Surveyor to the Fabric of St. Paul's wrote in a letter to the press:

'. . . St. Paul's stands on a thin bed of marl under which is over forty foot of loose sand and gravel held together by the presence of water; if this is tapped in any way, subsidence is bound to follow with what peril to the Cathedral I care not to predict . . . . Its vast untied spaces, its enormous weight brought to earth by a few piers and its exact equilibrium are safe only so long as the subsoil remains undisturbed. No proposal I have heard short of underpinning the whole area of the Cathedral and taking the foundations down to the clay some fifty foot below the present foundations would in my opinion safeguard the building. I cannot view so hazardous and expensive an undertaking without the gravest misgivings.'

Fortunately this project also was frustrated, and London's

Cathedral survives. The truth of this situation affecting St. Paul's and its foundations has now been fully digested and the possibility of further schemes threatening the Cathedral appear remote. However excavations under the City have already taken their toll, and the hammering taken by the beautiful Wren church of St. Stephen, Wallbrook has finally rendered the floor of the nave unsafe. The church stands between the Central and District underground railways, and even the old Wall Brook has been moled, thus reducing moisture in the subsoil.

In 1972 it was the turn of St. Paul's Cathedral to be given a massive face lift, and in the process a considerable amount of restoration work was done on the fabric; this all cost three million pounds. The Bath and Portland Group made a donation of 10,000 cubic feet of stone, weighing about 650 tons, towards the restoration work. The first consignment was to be brought to London in the Thames barge *May* under conditions simulating the contemporary conditions of Wren's time (see Plate 26). Unfortunately the new stone was not quarried from the same King's Quarry as the original stone, for most of Wren's stone had come from the northeast part of the Island which is now Crown property and used by the Admiralty.

In the early 1900's Thames barges plied regularly between London and Portland carrying loads ranging between 25 and 200 tons. Visitors to Portland can still see niches blasted into the rock face so that the bows of the barges could be beached against the cliffs. Here derricks (named for the macabre hangman of the 16th–17th century) mounted on the cliff edge were used to load the stone; these unsophisticated landing points are still used today by local fishermen. The sailing barge *May* was no stranger to Portland, for she was launched in 1891 and visited Castletown Pier many times in the early years of this century. Her last trip to Portland was in 1933 when her cargo of stone was 125 tons, but today she is licensed to carry only 50 tons of cargo to sea.

For her passage in 1972, she flew from her main mast the Kivel emblem of The Bath and Portland Group—a quarryman's cutting implement used in scappling (dressing) block stone surrounded by a circle, (see Fig. C). She was skippered by Reg Martin and her mate was Keith Stock. All went well, and when the barge arrived at St. Catherine's Dock on 11th August, she was met by the

Master and members of the Court of the Worshipful Company of Masons, who exercised their ancient right and prerogative to accept or reject any building stone coming into London. But there was a snag: for the whole enterprise might have been frustrated by a strike of the London dockers then proceeding. However the dockers collaborated; they ended their strike for a few hours especially to unload the *May* and indeed the dockers concerned made a gift of the wages they would have earned, amounting in all to some £40, to the St. Paul's Restoration Fund.

C. The kivel, emblem of The Bath and Portland Group.

When John Reay, the Group's Manager of the Portland quarries attended to assure the smooth running of events, he noticed that a half ton block of Portland stone bearing the personal 'wine-glass' mark of Sir Christopher Wren, which had been especially included in the cargo, was swinging nonchalantly over the dock. He urged the dockers' foreman to take special care, and by way of reinforcement asked if he had heard of Christopher Wren. For answer the foreman leaned perilously over the hold and called 'Chris—somone wants you.' The foreman then presented Christopher Wren—in person. It took this quick Cockney docker but a moment to recall that he was a direct descendant of the great architect, and when the £40 cheque was presented to the Very Reverend Martin Sullivan, Dean of St. Paul's, it was, of course, Christopher Wren who made the presentation.

10

———— ✦ ————

Roads, Canals and Railways

HISTORIANS HAVE DATED the beginning of the Industrial Revolution at the middle of the 18th century, because then
the harnessing of power enabled materials to be lifted, converted,
and transported mechanically. But there were antecedents without
which the Industrial Revolution could never have started. A
two-hundred-year period of remarkable development in the fields
of discovery, commerce, and finance, starting in the reign of
Queen Elizabeth I, created the conditions without which the value
of this power would have been of only minor significance.

It was in Elizabeth's reign that England assumed a national
consciousness, bringing her productive and social systems under
national control instead of municipal control; this applied particularly to conditions of trade and industry. Hers also were the
glorious days of the merchant adventurers; a new merchant
capitalism was displacing the two hundred year old guild system.
In its place came the joint stock companies such as the East India
Company and the African Company (to be followed two generations later by the Hudson's Bay Company) in which affairs were
conducted by the corporation as a whole for the benefit of
individual shareholders. Such companies were given monopolies
in their geographical spheres of operation. Up to the time of
Elizabeth the borrowing of money had been regarded as sinful and
contrary to religious teaching. But Elizabeth authorized the
borrowing of money for commercial and industrial development.
This meant that the enterprising merchants of the City of London
could develop their natural skills in industry and international

commerce at a rate greater than their personal funds would allow. This indeed could be said to be fundamental to the supremacy of the City in world finance.

Lines of communication had from pre-history been essential to trade development. First there was water—the sea and the rivers; then came tracks connecting the early island settlements: the best surviving example is the Icknield Way which wherever possible runs characteristically along the safer, chalky heights of the downlands. Next came the Roman roads such as the Fosse Way, Stayne Street and Watling Street, and 1600 years later came the turnpike roads and then the canals. The canals were to have only a short period of glory before they were superseded by the railways. Each transport system in its turn can be seen to be a logical step in the social and industrial development of England. Without communications the Industrial Revolution would have been a non-event.

A network of tracks connected the centres of early civilization, and much as the modern motorways have been superimposed on the older A and B road system, so the Romans laid down their road network between their camps. These roads, in the southern half of England often composed of oolitic limestones, were the only roads built with hard core prior to the turnpike roads of the 18th century. The principal Roman roads connected their five provincial governing settlements: Colchester, Gloucester, Lincoln, Verulamium (standing some half-mile from present day St. Albans), and York; and in the manner of Roman provincial development, little protection was provided from the Celts in the hinterland away from the camps and the roads themselves. But by encouraging the Celtic chiefs to emulate Roman methods, the Celt was romanized by his own goodwill. After the Romans had departed, and the Saxons who came next had done so much to obliterate Roman occupation, the feudal system emerged, and the crazy road pattern of rural England slowly took shape. When trade developed in Tudor times a considerable proportion of raw materials and goods were still transported by water, however, so that while the roads deteriorated, new ports came into being, created for and maintained by coastal traffic. In fact it has been said that Britain had a better national roadway system under the Saxons than it did under the Stuarts.

As trade developed so did industry, and the reign of Elizabeth is marked for great expansion of mining of many sorts. Iron was needed for the navy, particularly for cannons; coal was needed to replace wood as a domestic fuel, for wood was being consumed faster than it was produced by nature; from the Mendip hills came lead and from Cornwall and Devon came tin; while stone, often the oolitic limestones, became a general building material where previously it had been reserved only for church and royal buildings. Coal was not yet essential to industry, and as a substitute domestic fuel its use was limited to regions near to the pits or to navigable water. Thus 'sea-coal' was used generally in London and the Thames Valley and for the populations of coastal and riverside centres. The beautiful chimneys of Elizabethan manor houses bear testimony to the increased use of coal for domestic purposes.

The Stuart dynasty has been said to be 'an uneventful prolongation of the Elizabethan era.' Under the pacifist James I, the century-long domestic arguments and differences between England and Scotland continued without resolve, and peace came at last to settle the maritime warfare between England and Spain. This enabled the Virginia Company and the Massachusetts Bay Company to press forward with their policies of emigration, which had at their root the creation in America of a permanent market for English goods in exchange for American products, particularly tobacco from Virginia. Motivated by economic and religious ideals, the English went forth to lay the foundations not only of the United States of America but also of the British Empire. For all this, it was private enterprise that supplied the finance and initiative, while the role of government was merely to maintain the conditions under which colonization was possible.

Coal was not used heavily for industrial purposes until the later Stuart era. This was the first period of considerable increase in the coal trade, while a second increase occurred early in the 19th century—'the age of coal and iron'. Unhappily the development of the coal mining industry saw the sequestration of the capitalist employer from the manual worker—a characteristic which was to become general in later times. The very close relationship of Lord and commoner under the feudal system had shown far more humanity than could be seen in the selfish elements which surfaced during the first century of the Industrial Revolution and led on to the embattled strongholds of employer and employee.

Although industrial development was on the move, the state of the roads of Britain continued to be appalling, mainly for lack of any administrative machinery to keep them in repair. Parishes were legally bound to give six days a year of unpaid labour by farmers to the repair of roads, one farmer being selected as surveyor without state or even municipal supervision. By the later days of the Stuart era the roads were becoming a national disgrace, and it was in these circumstances that a few of the first turnpike roads were constructed by Acts of Parliament during the reign of James II. It is a paradox of history that when in the age of Queen Anne beautiful ships were already constructed to convey heavy goods to America and Asia, sacks of coal in England were still strapped to the sides of pack horses because wheeled traffic could not move on the muddy roads.

Thus the turnpike companies were granted Parliamentary powers to build roads and erect toll bars across them, where users paid their toll and went with doubtful safety upon their way. Four hundred Road Acts were passed between 1700 and 1750 and another 1600 Road Acts followed in the next 40 years. This was perhaps the most important gift of the Hanoverian epoch to the progress of the Industrial Revolution. It is notable that as the roads improved so the weight of carriages and wagons was reduced. And it is not surprising (for we still see it today) that as the road network improved so the traffic increased to match it. It became the fashion for the English to travel for the sake of travel over the whole of the network (and indeed to spill all over the continent of Europe). One effect of this was to crowd the City of Bath in the days of Beau Nash to such an extent that it was decided to re-build its streets 'in a style befitting the solid splendour and comfort of that age.' In a census of 1801, Bath already had 30,000 inhabitants and was ninth in size of all English cities.

McAdam was the engineering genius of road building and by constant experiment he produced the metal turnpike road surfaces which bear his name to this day. Macadam was creating for the future a permanent market for crushed igneous rock. The later turnpikes enjoyed a relatively short period of usefulness before the railway system of the 19th century came into being. By 1840, 22,000 miles of good turnpike roads had been built throughout England and there were some 8000 toll gates and side bars. Now the wagon supplemented the pack horse and the highways rang to the chime of bells on the harness of dray horses, giving precedence to wagon teams over all other traffic. Off the turnpikes, the rolling by-roads of England were taking their pattern not from Chesterton's rolling English drunkard, but from the enclosures they were having to skirt.

As public consciousness turned to the improvement in the highway system, so it turned to the improvement of 'inland navigation'. The Duke of Bridgewater, like many other aristocrats, owned coal mines, and in a desire to link his Worsley collieries with Manchester he used his Parliamentary influence and his capital to build the Bridgewater Canal. At his elbow was the half illiterate engineer Brindley. This strange partnership started the movement by which all England was rapidly netted with waterways. Hills and valleys were no obstacle. Tunnels pierced the Pennines and Cotswolds, aqueducts carried the canals over valleys, and lock waters bore the narrowboats up and down the hills of England. The Manchester–Liverpool canal was completed in the 1760's and in the next 10 years, the Duke and his engineer built the Grand Junction canal joining the rivers Mersey and Trent. The building of the Avon canal which connected the Avon with the River Thames was to open up the market for Bath stone, as will be seen.

The building of the canals themselves created a temporary market for block stone. More significant however, is the emergence in canal building of William Smith (q.v.), who was to do so much to establish the science of geology. Traffic on the canals travelled toll-free, and the existence of these early waterways and those that immediately followed did much to put down monopolies in the corn trade; for communication was soon open between Liverpool, Bristol and Hull and ran through counties abundant in grain.

The canal and turnpike road systems combined to enhance both home and overseas trade. By enabling heavy goods, particularly minerals, to travel from the centre of England to the ports, a balance of trade resulted which enabled a much wider range of imports to be brought back. Originally imports had been luxuries for the rich such as wine, silks, and spices; but now goods for general consumption were brought from overseas so that tea and coffee became beverages for all classes, and sugar was generally available too. The long haul, which through the next 200 years was to do so much to emancipate the working class, had started.

But the canals built by the 'navvies' (as the inland navigators who constructed them were called), were to have only a short period of usefulness, for between the years 1830 and 1870 came the age of railways (see Plate 28). The railways, 'England's gift to the world', originated from experiments in the removal of coal from pithead to stockground sites at the collieries. The principle of moving traffic over pre-determined tracks goes back into antiquity, for the ancient Greeks had used rutways for the movement of religious equipment; by the 18th century the plateway, along which traffic was guided by flanged wheels, came into use. The first absolutely authenticated example of the 'flanged wheel and edge-rail' system was on Ralph Allen's Prior Park wagonway at Bath which was opened about 1730 to bring stone down from his quarries high on Combe Down to the Avon navigation. A similar system was used by John Curr in 1776 at Sheffield colliery, but in this case the plateway accommodated common carts with plain wheels; this could be described as a form of tramway which of course did not precede the invention of the flanged wheel and edge-rail system, as is sometimes thought. The Merchant Railway at Portland (q.v.) was another early example of railway development.

Although earlier railways had been approved by Act of Parliament, the first public railway to embark upon steam traction was the Stockton and Darlington railway which came into being in 1821 through the driving force of Edward Pease. The railway opened in September 1825 with $26\frac{3}{4}$ miles of track. Even then the passenger coaches, which resembled contemporary stage coaches, were horse-drawn until 1833. Meanwhile the Liverpool and Manchester Railway Company had opened in September 1830 and carried 72,000 passengers, 2650 tons of coal and 1450 tons of freight in its first year; passenger receipts were some 10 times greater than those budgeted, and freight was about 60% greater than budget.

From there on the railway network grew apace. Although the many railway companies were independent of each other, most tracks were built widely to a standard gauge of four feet eight-and-one-half inches, and probably had its origin in traction by horse working in shafts. However, Brunel, engineer of the Great Western Railway and builder of Box Tunnel (q.v.), selected a gauge of seven foot naught-and-one-quarter inches in his search for greater efficiency, thus bringing about a 'battle of the gauges' between the GWR and the other railway companies. After various early experiments in railway track foundation, igneous rock 'flints' were eventually adopted as the standard ballast.

Government regulation was of course necessary to the development of the railway system; first came the Regulation of Railways Act 1840 which dealt with safety; and in 1844 Gladstone's Act provided that a minimum of one train per day should run at an average speed of over 12 miles per hour with fares of one penny per mile. In 1842 the principal railway companies themselves set up the Railway Clearing House which enabled cross traffic between the different railway systems to run on a basis of 'through' fares and freights, with an equitable division of revenue. By 1860 the railway monopoly of inland transport became almost absolute. However, the method of its finance was to bring about an all-important change in company law, and to appreciate how this came about it is necessary to turn back to the days of Elizabeth I.

The medieval 'regulated company' had been in the nature of a trade guild affording protection and often some measure of monopoly to members who traded on their own account. This type of unincorporated company was largely superseded in the reign of Elizabeth I by the joint stock companies of which the first were the Russian Company, the Levant Company and the African Company, shortly followed by the East India Company and later the Hudson's Bay Company. Towards the end of the 17th century the principle of granting charters to joint stock companies trading overseas was extended to companies trading at home, such as banking and certain manufacturing companies. The first joint stock bank was the Bank of England, incorporated in 1694, but as yet charters were not easy to obtain and were erroneously identified with monopolies only granted in the public interest.

During the 18th century however, un-incorporated companies became very numerous and speculation in share dealings was rife. The result was the Act known as the Bubble Act of 1719 which made it an indictable offence to open books and make stock transferable unless the company were incorporated by Royal Charter. This was the first recognition of the necessary distinction between private and public company procedures. Despite this however the South Sea Bubble burst in the following year causing a long delay to the development of joint stock companies. The Bubble Act forced unincorporated companies which had previously used public funds to become incorporated by grant of Charter. The canal companies were the first companies formed under the new mode, shortly followed by gas companies and then the railway companies, and this form of company became customary for public utilities.

In the second quarter of the 19th century nearly 600 Acts of Parliament were passed for promoting new railway lines and another 500 for extensions and enlargements of existing lines or for granting amended powers. The capital authorized during that period was in excess of £350,000,000—far more than had ever been put into any other single channel of investment. £233,000,000 were authorized in the three years 1845 to 1847, the second period of massive expansion of 'railway mania'. There was no provision in Company law during the earlier stages of railway development for limited liability of shareholders except as a special concession. The passing of the Joint Stock Companies Act of 1844, which dealt extensively with rules for company regulation, still left the joint stock company shareholder as a partner with unlimited liability for all its members. But the railways required special protection from the public which could only be procured by Act of Parliament, and thus their costs in statutory legislation soared considerably.

The passing of an Act constituting a railway a 'Parliamentary Company', conferred on the shareholders the privilege of limited liability and this was the factor which attracted very substantial investment in the railways during their period of development. The railway companies were thus the first to have very large bodies of shareholders. But the growth of railway investment on the basis of limited liability brought complaints from firms needing capital for other purposes; these complaints were largely based upon unfair advantage and the diversion of too much money to the railways.

In the forefront of those complaining were representatives of the iron industry and their complaints became louder in the later 1850's on the introduction of Bessemer's mild steel. This in itself was an important railway development, for the new steel rail lasted much longer than the old iron rail; in fact steel replaced iron so rapidly that the iron industry was quickly transformed into a steel industry, based first on Bessemer's mild steel and later on Siemen's open hearth process, the latter introduced in the 1860s. So finally the Limited Liability Act of 1855 was passed, limiting the liability of members of all incorporated companies to the amount unpaid on their shares. Quite clearly Parliamentary pressure in these changes was brought about by the iron and steel industry, through their resentment of the railway privileges under the parliamentary company system.

The next major act was the Companies Act of 1862 which is generally regarded as the foundation of British company law. It was largely a consolidating Act however, though it did introduce the principle of absolute prohibition of alteration of the objects clause in a company's memorandum of association; all companies registered under the Act thus became subject to the doctrine of *ultra vires*. It was under this Act of 1862 that the seven partnerships in the stone quarrying and stone masonry industries in the region of Bath joined together as The Bath Stone Firms Limited in 1887.

The merger acknowledged a truth: industry was growing and public utilities were consolidating, so that selling had to be geared on a national basis. The Bath Stone Firms were therefore following a principle that, however altruistic it may sound, was and is nonetheless logical. For instead of exhausting their energy in petty competition, they were now able to devote it to giving bigger customers a better service and a broader availability of products and skills.

11

---·ৠ·---

Regency Bath

THE CITY OF BATH survived from Norman times until the 18th century largely by virtue of the wool trade and the lingering interest in the decaying Roman Baths; each took turns in maintaining life in the community. The wool trade had originated in East Anglia with the arrival of the Flemings from Belgium; it was worked on the guild system which was taking shape during the second half of the 14th century. Prior to this, the production of wool had been a cottage industry in which wives and sometimes all the family bent over the spinning wheel. The wool trade expanded from East Anglia to Yorkshire, and then to the West country where weaving, already a coveted craft, resulted in the addition of a weaver's shuttle to the arms of Bath Abbey in the 14th century; Chaucer's Wife of Bath was a weaver 'very skilful in cloth making'. During the 15th century Cotswold wool was held to be supreme in England and throughout Europe; it was responsible for prosperity in the West, where 'the record still stands in magnificent stone farm houses and old fulling-mills beside the valley streams'.

A major boom in the cloth trade occurred in the second half of the 14th century as the manufacture and export of cloth grew at the expense of the export of raw wool. The clothing guilds in the great towns therefore attempted to prevent competition from the rural industry by prohibiting their merchants from dealing in country cloth, but this only underlined their opposing interests and they were unsuccessful. So the great merchants operated on a capitalist system, in which the raw material of wool was supplied to village craftsmen who had their own looms; the woven cloth was passed back to the merchants and on to finishing processes before reaching the market.

Daniel Defoe was later to observe that 'many of the great families who now pass for gentry in the western counties have been originally raised from and built up by this truly noble manufacture of cloth.' This 'manufacture of cloth' increased in the last quarter of the 15th century, and the West Country enjoyed 50 years of prosperity; but the weaving industry went into decline at the time of the Dissolution—a double blow to Bath which had of course also been an ecclesiastical centre. From that time on, Bath had to depend more on her hot springs. But the cloth trade was by no means dead, and survived at the expense of the Stapling system for the export of raw wool which declined severely; when Calais was lost, just before Elizabeth came to the throne, the vital Wool Staple of Calais was barred to the English Staplers, and there was a consequent loss in wool exports. This rapidly worsened as markets in Bruges and Antwerp were also closed. It was at this point that the English, with their typical fortitude and imagination, formed new trading companies in the City of London to establish markets for wool in the Baltic, Turkey, the Levant, and Russia. This was at the beginning of the great era of merchant adventurers; mainly they were the wealthy enterprising merchants of the City of London, who were perhaps the first to think of the world as a nut ripe for cracking.

Only in Elizabeth's time, according to Camden, did the medicinal spa come back into its own in place of the holy well, and to quote David Gadd 'it were as if in the intervening centuries Bath had lost its way in history and now assumed once more its true role'. Buxton, in Derbyshire, was becoming a fashionable resort where the nobility came to drink its waters and the Earl of Shrewsbury was developing fine lodgings there to attract visitors to the Spa. Bath however had only very squalid accommodation and although its waters were famous it was by no means in fashion; despite the continuing trade in cloth, the West of England was to remain very low in order of wealth compared with the rest of the country.

At the beginning of Queen Elizabeth's reign the hot waters of Bath were drunk by those whose internal diseases required them, and such patients were supplied with water ladled from the full cisterns early in the morning, whilst the baths were clean and before the bathers arrived, for bathing in the hot waters was also a principal use at that time. Dr. Jones laid it down as a rule in his 'Bathes of Bathes Ayde' that patients immediately after drinking the water 'should walk gently a few paces in a temperate air.' He also suggested that bathers should approach the hottest part of the bath by 'little and little', and directed that they should 'instantly rise out of the water upon the least symptoms of fainting.'

Dr. William Turner, Dean of Wells and chief physician to King Edward VI, composed a book of the baths of England, Germany, and Italy during the time of his banishment under Queen Mary. Therein he suggested that the Baths of Bath were 'in very little esteem; even less than those of Buxton in Derbyshire.' According to Dr. Turner, people of fortune went to foreign baths when they required the use of hot medicinal waters. But he gave Bath priority, and upon publication of his book in the year 1562 the English began to frequent their own hot fountains, and Bath acquired such a reputation that the Cross bath was soon reserved only for 'the better sort of people'; the Hot Bath, called some-times the Common Bath and sometimes the Long Bath, being the only cistern that remained for common use.

The publication of Dr. Turner's book and the endeavours of Dr. Jones caused the court of France to retaliate by restoring the baths of Bourbon l'Anci. These restorations in France in turn led Queen Elizabeth to take interest in the public baths of Bath. By a charter dated the 14th September 1590 the Queen confirmed the lease of the baths to the Corporation of Bath, making the Corporation the perpetual guardians of the City and of its hot waters. By this charter William Sherston was declared Bath's first mayor: having rented Burton farm in the parish of Walcot, Burton House was the first to bear the new regalia of the city. The citizens of Bath immediately extended their boundaries into the hundred of Bathforum as well as over the precincts of the monastery dissolved by Henry VIII. They set about the task of promoting the baths and soon the City was famed as much for her baths as for her trade in cloth manufacture.

After the Elizabethan charter, the Hot Bath was barred from use by the common people and at the same time a new cistern was built on its west side to receive its overflowing waters and serve as a bath for the use of the diseased poor, who had now been expelled from the Cross Bath as well. This cistern, some 10 feet in length from north to south and eight feet in breadth, took the name of the Lepers' Bath; it was accommodated with a small room for the bathers to strip and dress themselves, and the suite in process of time was called the Lepers' Hospital. The Lepers' Bath enjoyed an unwelcome popularity, for the 'beggars of Bath' became a byword. It was a custom for local parish authorities to send their sick to Bath or Buxton at the expense of the parish, and as some of these poor remained after their cure, a right to residence and poor relief could be established. This became a popular method of ridding towns of their unwanted indigents. Once settled in Bath these paupers lived by begging, and the practice became so common that Acts of Parliament for the control of vagrancy were passed in the 16th century. The 'Beggars of Bath' were a recognized social category and 'go to Bath' became a cliche to dismiss importunate beggars from doorways anywhere in England.

The King's Bath, which had been built in the 12th century for the Bishop's royal guests, had also come into use some 20 years before Queen Elizabeth's charter and when a drinking fountain was installed in this bath, its use by wealthy invalids increased steadily. To meet the influx of bathers the City built a new bath adjoining the King's Bath to 'serve for women severally', meaning separately from the King's Bath; but in the absence of women, men were to have resort to this new bath in such order as the mayor and justices of Bath or their officers should appoint (see Plate 21).

The new bath was finished in 1576, and at the beginning of the 17th century became known as the Queen's Bath when Anne of Denmark, James I's queen, made two visits to Bath seeking a cure for dropsy. On the second occasion, when Anne was in the King's Bath, a sudden flame is said to have shot up from the water and spread over the surface, which discouraged the Queen from taking further cures there. In the early 17th century the city authorities had trouble with nude mixed bathing and endeavoured in vain to seek the aid of the Privy Council to stop it. Samuel Pepys when he paid a visit to the baths in 1668 was not worried, and when visiting the Cross bath at four o'clock in the morning apparently enjoyed the sight of the fine ladies bathing with him.

By this time Bath was a city of some 250 houses with a population of less than 1200: there were within its ancient walls weavers who still dried their wool on racks on a site where Milsom Street stands today. The mayor in 1662 complained that 'we are a very little poore citie', but in spite of the decaying houses the City was to survive. Perhaps the visit of Charles II in 1677 with his Queen Katherine of Braganza, made in the hope that the waters would help her to produce an heir to the throne, was a turning point. The treatment was successful, and the King enjoyed his visit well enough to pay subsequent visits—not so much with the Queen, but rather with his mistresses. Later, visits were paid by James II and by his daughter Princess Anne and her husband Prince George of Denmark, so that a tradition of visits from royalty had been set up by the turn of the 18th century. 'Everyone', said Swift, 'is going to Bath'.

Nude bathing had gone by this time, and some orderliness of procedure in the baths was forming. Bath lacked the amenities for the company it was attracting however, and eventually the city authorities started to make small concessions to the refined taste of its fashionable society, and a Master of Ceremonies was appointed. The fate of Bath was indeed in the balance having on the one hand a clientele of wealthy visitors and on the other a poverty-stricken population and a dilapidated town. Then came a remarkable deal from that old cardsharper destiny. In the space of a generation there came to the City three unlikely characters, of whom each needed the other two, and all three were essential to Bath: Nash made it fashionable; Wood made it beautiful; and Allen made it possible.

First to arrive, in 1705, was Beau (Richard) Nash, a 29 year old gambler from London. He came to gamble, and only took over as Master of Ceremonies when Captain Webster, his predecessor, was killed duelling over a gambling dispute. Nash may have been motivated to some extent by self interest when he concluded that taking the waters for medicinal purposes was a dull thing without entertainment, for he forthwith set about turning Bath into a centre combining medicine with pleasure. Nash has been described by Brian Little as 'the spiritual ancestor of Blackpool,

Eastbourne, Miami and Monte Carlo.' Let it be said, however, that the municipal authority at Bath was not unaware of the opportunities its wealthy and aristocratic visitors afforded. The Pump Room, the dream of Dr. William Oliver, was already mooted before Nash arrived, and the concept of a better City was slowly developing; but that concept had nothing of the grandiose plans that were soon to unfold (see Plate 24). Nash saw that the Pump Room was rapidly built, and went about the business of pressing for the Assembly Rooms, completed by Thomas Harrison in 1708. Needless to say this was firstly a house for cards and tea, and its ballroom came later, in 1720.

Nash was an orderly if unsuccessful gambler, and no cheat; and the disciplines he imposed on visitors were blunt and strict. Among his many rules was a code of conduct at public assemblies and balls. This code tended to mix good taste with pedantry, yet perhaps it was necessary in a society not without its Malaprops. 'That Gentlemen of Fashion never appearing in a Morning before the Ladies in Gowns and Caps, show Breeding and Respect' was clearly an admonition not intended for gentlemen of fashion who would know better; and 'That the Elder Ladies and Children be contented with a Second Bench at the ball, as being past, or not come to Perfection' reveals even less style in its author than in the more unworldly visitors to the Ball for whom it was intended.

Nash also instituted a control on gambling, and prohibitions on wearing swords in the City, and on duelling. Though of humble birth, Nash had the style that enabled him to master his superiors, and his eccentric attire—a white hat, black wig and brown beaver habit, ever surrounding his increasingly ruddy complexion—came to be regarded as a livery of authority. Though Nash faded with time to become virtually a pauper at his death in 1761, it was he who had started a brilliant era and kept it going for half a century.

Next to arrive after Nash was Ralph Allen, a young man of 18, from Cornwall. He came in 1712 to take up the duties of Assistant Postmaster, for which task he had some previous experience with his family at St. Colomb. Allen found an appalling measure of dishonesty and inefficiency in the postal service; after helping General Wade who was engaged in anti-Jacobite activities in Bath, Allen received Wade's backing enabling him to take control of the 'cross posts', as the Bye-way and Cross-road Postal Services were called. The Post Office had contracted with the right man: the service became efficient, and Allen went on his way to making a fortune. Allen married Wade's illegitimate daughter, thus following a custom among the wealthy where bastard daughters were often married off on 'humbly descended young men on the make.' As Wade died a bachelor, there was no other issue to claim preference over his daughter, and this added further to Allen's wealth.

Allen was a man of remarkable parts. He had a great sense of public duty as well as a flair for finance. In 1727 he purchased the limestone quarries at Combe Down on the site of ancient Camalodunum, with the three objects of rebuilding Bath, exporting stone to other parts of the country, and providing regular employment under better conditions than had previously obtained. Allen went on to be Mayor of Bath in 1742, leading the council with such vigour and supremacy that it gained the title of the 'one-headed corporation'. Partly through the influence of General Wade, who was Member for Bath from 1722 until his death, Allen rose in society and numbered William Pitt, Fielding, Warburton, Pope, Gainsborough and David Garrick among his intimate friends.

Alexander Pope, the 'little monster of the Jacobites' had a great regard for the hospitable and charitable Allen who made him welcome through many seasons at Prior Park. The only difference that separated them came near Pope's death and arose over Pope's beloved Martha Blount. Allen's wife Gertrude had objected to the blatantly intimate behaviour of the unmarried pair under her roof; Allen endeavoured to heal the breach, putting the matter down to a misunderstanding between the ladies; he travelled to London to see Pope, but in vain. It was Pope, as may be imagined, who had the last word; he left Allen £150 in his will, his assessment of the value of near half a lifetime of munificent hospitality. With disdain Allen handed the cash to charity.

Of the great triumvirate John Wood was the last to arrive in Bath and the first to die. In 1725 Wood, a young surveyor working in Yorkshire, sent to Allen a set of plans for the development of Bath; they were his passport to fame. The plans were inspired by work Wood had been doing for Lord Chandos in

London and Lord Bingley in Yorkshire. Wood's architectural style differed from that of the Wren school which had by then persisted for a quarter of a century. Wren had followed mainly French lines, only conceding a minor and late acknowledgement of the Italian school as *intaglios* became available. Wood was inspired by the Italian school of André Palladio of Vicenza, the late Renaissance architect who succeeded in simulating the ancient orders of Roman architecture. Palladio became the high fashion in the early Georgian era, when Lord Burlington in 1715 brought to England Giacomo Leoni, a Venetian architect, to edit an edition of Palladio's designs. The five orders of the Palladian system were Roman Doric, Tuscan, Ionic, Corinthian, and Composite (being a mixture of Ionic and Corinthian). Yet sensibly Wood also followed the mathematical formulae of Wren that had done so much to bring elegant proportion to building design and standardization to construction. John Wood was the answer to Ralph Allen's prayer. With Wood's exquisite taste he could now cater for the society that Nash was attracting to Bath. Wood was to design a 'new Rome', but sadly it was left to his son to bring the plan to completion.

When John Wood arrived in Bath two years later, he noted the condition of the houses and their contents which were the essential accommodation of the wealthy visitors to the spa. The chimney pieces, hearths and slabs were all of free stone, 'daily cleaned by a particular whitewash which, by paying tribute to everything that touched it, soon rendered the brown floors like the starry firmament.' The floorboards were 'made of a brown colour, with soot and small beer to hide the dirt as well as their own imperfections.' The doors were slight and thin and the best locks had only varnished fitments. The principal rooms were furnished with cane or rush bottomed chairs, 'each chair seldom exceeding three half crowns in value, nor were the tables or chests of drawers better in their kind.' The weekly price of lodgings so furnished was 10 shillings a room during the season and at the same time garrets for servants yielded five shillings apiece, and out of season these prices were reduced to one half.

As buildings improved during John Wood's first 20 years in Bath, carpets were introduced to cover the floors and the rooms were all wainscoted and painted in a costly and handsome manner.

Cane and rush chairs gave way to 'walnut tree chairs, some with leather and some with damask bottoms.' Bedding, curtains, and linen for table all improved till they 'became suitable even for people of the highest rank.' The cost of lodgings received no advance, perhaps because the seasons were lengthened almost every year. Bath in 1734 is shown on the endpaper.

The sets of rooms known as Linsay's and Wiltshire's built under Wood's direction were completed in 1728. By this time the thatched roofs of Bath were already giving way to stone built houses of several storeys, incorporating the type of sash windows first used by Philip Taylor at the end of the 17th century. Wood was a master of linear rather than area planning and this can be seen in the geometry of Queen Square (see Plate 22) and in the beautiful lines rising up the hill towards the Circus and Royal Crescent. Wood perfected the architecture of 'the terrace' which was exploited for the first time on a grand scale in Bath; he also created the terraced crescent, for terraces had previously been straight. In this Bath led the world. It was John Wood who gave Nash his ideas for the development of Regent's Park and St. James's Park in London.

Wood also had the idea of the parade or promenade where the fashionable could disport themselves and display their fine clothes. A grand parade south of Queen Square had been part of his plan for the new Rome, though it was never carried out. But Wood's parade became the model for countless esplanades and seafronts throughout the country and indeed abroad. Queen Square had provided a formal garden but no space for walking. Now two parades to the south-east of the old city—closer to the Assembly Rooms of Beau Nash—gave freedom from traffic, mud, and 'the baser animals'. These two parades, the North and South Parades, were regarded as Wood's greatest contribution to the amenities of Bath. Certain of his fantasies were never fulfilled: these included the Royal Forum and Imperial Gymnasia, intended for sports and the practice of medicinal exercises. There was however a further gift that John Wood had made to the City: for on his death his son, John Wood the Younger, came to prominence. The son was in the opinion of many a finer architect than his father, and worked to beautify Bath at a time when the high fashion was already starting to fade, and a new more rigid society was taking its place.

The idea of connecting the rivers Avon and Thames had been

first mooted in the reign of Queen Elizabeth I, and was reconsidered by Oliver Cromwell after the Civil Wars. During the reigns of Charles II and Queen Anne the project was further promoted but objections were strong and numerous, and finally the Canal was not to be opened until 1810. Meanwhile the Duke of Beaufort at his own expense procured an Act of Parliament in 1711 for making the Avon navigable between Bath and Bristol. It took 16 years—13 of them wasted—for the first barge, laden with deal boards, pig-lead and meal to be brought up to Bath. Under the Act the 'duty' on goods carried between Bath and Bristol was not to exceed five shillings a tun. The tun rates varied from the beginning; for light goods such as hay, straw and wool, two shillings and sixpence; for 'ponderous goods' such as wood, wine and grain, two shillings; and for freestone, 18 pence 'per tun of twenty cubical feet'.

When Ralph Allen purchased the freestone quarries at Combe Down, work had recently been completed to render the River Avon navigable downstream. It was this access to the port of Bristol by water that encouraged Allen to pursue the export of his stone to other areas. But the cost of transporting the stone from the quarry on the hill to the Avon bank below it was a barrier. Allen therefore determined to 'make such a road between the summit of the hill and the River Avon as the gentlemen in the north of England had made between their collieries and the River Tyne.' This was intended to reduce the cost to 'half the price of carrying it down in common wagons.' Evidently Allen with characteristic thoroughness obtained proper models of the roads and carriages used in the north, and indeed he found a mechanic who was able to improve on the original. The cost of stone reaching the river level was accordingly reduced, but not by the full hundred per cent. It now sold at three quarters of the old price—'seven shillings and sixpence a tun of twenty cubical feet.'

The ancient freestone quarries at the back of Camalodunum were 'subterraneous caverns which had been dug from time to time in the brow of the mountain to produce wrought stone for buildings and small ornaments to embellish them, as well as for making courtyards and gardens.' As accidents frequently happened in these old mines, Allen began to dig for stone in a new quarry 'open from the top', and this is undoubtedly the Combe

Down quarry associated with his name today. The refuse was such that 'part was burnt into lime, part served for building common walls, some was cut into slabs for paving floors, and the rest was converted into steps and such other things as were proper to be made with a harder stone than ordinary.' This enabled Allen to blend the good and bad stone together, though John Wood said this brought disgrace on a material which when properly quarried was 'in truth fit for the walls of a palace for the greatest Prince in Europe.'

Having entered the freestone business with a view to reducing its price, Allen immediately entered the domestic masons' trade in Bath. He proposed to lower the rates by saving the time the workmen lost in going between their homes in or about the city and the quarries in the external brow of Camalodunum. He also improved conditions by finding them constant employment and paying them their wages regularly every week. To achieve all this, Allen built houses on top of the down for those concerned in digging, raising, and transporting the unwrought stone down to a common yard by the side of the River Avon; and for the masons employed in the yard, he built proper sheds to work under, as well as houses near it to live in. For this purpose John Wood made designs for two 'small towns' to receive the two sets of people thus employed, and as a result, the price of freestone work for local use was lowered by about 10%.

Allen's highmindedness regarding prices ran him into trouble: Milo Smith, one of the proprietors of the navigation, became a competitor in the trade for a time, but soon failed. Also Allen lacked freight for the export of block stone from time to time, and the chief master masons of the country reduced their prices below the levels to which Allen had abated them. Thus Allen found himself with considerable opposition, and had great difficulty in introducing the freestone into the London market, where some of his opponents maliciously compared Bath stone with Cheshire cheese 'liable to breed maggots that would soon devour it.'

When Greenwich Hospital was to be built, the architect, Colin Campbell, and the Clerk of the Works of the hospital were so prejudiced against Bath stone that a public meeting of the Governors was held at Salters' Hall in the City of London in the spring of 1728. There Bath stone was represented as a material 'unable to bear any weight, of a coarse texture, bad colour, and almost as dear as Portland stone for a public work in or near London'. John Wood says he was present when this representation was made, and, anticipating some such attack, had caused a Bath mason to attend with a sample of each sort of stone. The Governors ordered the patterns to be laid on the table before them, and Campbell, by himself mistaking one stone for the other, gave 'a notorious proof of his partiality, which led the Governors into an enquiry concerning the masons' trade.' But the result was to enable the Governors to contract for their new work in Portland stone upon terms a full 33% below what they had formerly paid for it.

This great abatement in price entirely defeated Allen's proposals for carrying out the masonry work of the Hospital with his stone. Deploring the reflections cast upon the freestone of Bath, Allen resolved to exhibit the stone in a seat which he determined to build for himself near his works and 'to much greater advantage and in much greater variety of uses than it had ever appeared in any other structure.' This led to the construction of the beautiful Prior Park at Combe Down (see Plate 22 and Fig. 5 page 227).

John Wood was retained by Allen, and submitted several designs in which 'the Orders of Architecture were to shine forth in all their glory.' The position of the mansion was selected to have 'a prospect as beautiful as a compact City at the bottom of a rich vale surrounded with fertile hills can possibly furnish the eye with.' It stands today as Wood had conceived it, above the village of Widcombe and the Avon 'to see all Bath and for all Bath to see'. The central mansion is flanked on each side by a Pavilion and a wing for various utilities. Wood fell out with Allen during the building of Prior Park, so that only the central mansion and the western arc were built by him, the eastern arc being completed later by Jones, who was Allen's Clerk of the Works.

Wood first built the westward wing of offices, composed of a principal and half storey, 172 feet in length by 34 feet in depth, to contain three coach houses, six stables, a harness room, barn, granaries, a hay house and pigeon house. Though Wood had intended that this building should be roofed in Cornish slate on timber, Allen insisted that nothing but stone was used for its covering. Freestone was used even for lining the inner walls of the stables. The pavilion, between the westward wing and the mansion, was built 'partly for coaches to stop under and partly for pigeons to reside in.' This structure is 34 feet square, the roof topped with a dome and an ornament consisting of a base, ball, balustrade and vane, all rising to some 60 feet. Here the pigeons are magnificently housed in cells all made of wrought freestone. 'Mr. Allen's pigeons', said Wood, 'will in all probability never desert their present place of abode.'

The mansion itself extends some 147 feet in length and 80 feet in depth, and for its support about 800 tons of large blocked freestone was buried, and wrought freestone was used for the outer and inner walls and stairs; and 'so that defects in other great houses from plastered walls are effectually removed in this', the several rooms and passages were also vaulted over in freestone. Wood, had to give thought to the sinking of the building during construction just as Wren had done with St. Paul's Cathedral. He concluded that 'by erecting the freestone walls with large stones in equal courses both within and without, they became equally strong on both sides' and thus able to support, and not buckle under, the weight of incumbent work.

The whole of the basement storey was paved with calcined, shelly, rag-stone from the rag of the quarry. 'This', said Wood, 'is the very strata that makes the roof of subterraneous quarries: and the next layer under it, commonly called the picking bed, is generally as much softer than good freestone as the rag is harder.' The basement housed the whole gamut of service rooms, from servants' hall to beer cellars and wine vaults: laundry to bakehouse and dairy: and of course kitchen and sculleries: larder and pantry. At the principal and chamber storey levels all the rooms were again built of freestone. The central feature of the principal storey was the grand portico with the superb view of Bath to the north. The suite to its east included a parlour, study, and chapel: to its west a dining room, drawing room, and principal staircase. Later the stone ornaments of the parlour and dining room were cut off to give way to wood panelling.

Wood commented on the whole of the central and western pile: 'The perambulation for the curious was thus designed. After viewing the stables in the simplicity of the Doric dress, and coming under a pavilion, great in its kind, the publick were to enter an Ionic gallery which would have the effect of a vast long stage to a rich theatre; and this leading them to the stone passage that traverses the basement storey of the house, from thence they were to descend to a stone hall of the Corinthean order and then pass into the stupendous portico of the same order.' The tour continued through the gallery of the chamber storey to the Tribunal Seat of the Chapel where 'cherubims and palm trees placed alternately gave them an idea of the manner in which King Solomon finished the inside of his Temple in Jerusalem' (see Plate 23).

The great house brought fame to Bath stone and to Allen's quarries. It also brought enquiries in abundance, and for five years Wood received from Allen a fee for dealing with them. Said Wood: 'But the good consequence to the stone trade from all the information that people were gratified with, was trifling in respect to the trouble of composing it; and I have the justest reasons to lament that my time had not been better employed.' Prior Park became a Roman Catholic boys' school in 1829 and though gutted by fire in 1836, the masonry survived entire, and has since been subjected only to changes fitting to the new use of the mansion.

In 1754 John Wood died, followed by Beau Nash in 1761 and George Allen in 1764. With them the magic of fashionable Bath seemed also to die. Yet, illogically, many of the finest buildings in the City were yet to rise, and the superb terraced buildings of Bath were not conceived until the third and fourth quarters of the 18th century. Slowly John Wood the Younger came into his own. In 1767 the building of his Royal Crescent began and by 1769 he had built the new Assembly Rooms. These 'Upper' Assembly Rooms instantly put Wiltshire's out of business, leaving Simpson's 'Lower' rooms to struggle on until extinguished by a fire in 1820. The Upper Assembly Rooms brought fashion to the upper town which, according to authoritarian views, was connected with the old town by a master plan of Wood the Younger. The Royal Crescent, completed in 1775, has an international reputation for its sheer beauty which sets off the most perfect natural prospect that Bath has to offer (see Plate 24). Wood the Younger had built the Circus meanwhile.

Now Thomas Baldwin, a young man in his middle 20's, came on the scene. From 1763 the Corporation of the City had been determined to build a new Guildhall, and Thomas Atwood the City Surveyor, to whom Baldwin was assistant, progressively defeated the proposals and plans set up by one architect after another. Finally it was Atwood's death which gave Baldwin the chance he had waited for; though Baldwin's designs followed the new Adams school rather than the Palladian so much favoured by the Woods, his Guildhall built between 1775 and 1778, was a masterpiece and, within it, the banqueting hall is exceptional.

Baldwin had assessed the advantages opened up when Robert Adam in 1769 accepted a commission from Sir William Pulteney to design and build the Pulteney Bridge over the Avon; thus connecting Pulteney's Bathwick estate with the City centre. Though it was intended that Adams should continue with the development of Bathwick, Pulteney died and it eventually fell to Baldwin to do so. By now City Surveyor, Baldwin went on to redesign the Roman baths precinct, in the course of which the Cross Bath and the superb Bath Street colonnade were built (see Plate 25). Late-comers into the creative scene in the last years of the 18th century were John Palmer, who designed St. James's Square and Lansdown Crescent, and completed the reconstruction of the Pump Room started by Baldwin; John Eveleigh, who built Camden Crescent and Grosvenor Place; and John Pinch, who created Cavendish Crescent and Sion Hill Place.

It was during this period of building development, the 1790's, that England reacted to the French Revolution; financial chaos ensued, and the builders of Bath went into bankruptcy. But the city which had been fashioned and clothed in the limestones of Wiltshire through 2000 years, was indestructible, and that it would survive was self-evident. The population during the 18th century had risen twentyfold, and though the need for new buildings abated, the accommodation provided by the Georgian buildings was fully occupied. Bath had become a convenient and entertaining place of retirement. It was to take one and a half centuries for a new industry, tourism, to make a new assessment of Bath's historic culture and architectural beauty, and bring with it a new prosperity.

12

---— ❧ ———

An Industry Built on Setts

WHILE BATH LAY watching the Industrial Revolution gather impetus, the ports round the estuaries of the Wirral and the industrial centres in Cheshire, Lancashire, and Yorkshire were forging ahead on the new wave of mechanization. Indeed, if 'revolution' be the right word, this was the very centre of revolt. The 19th century saw the Revolution in full cry, and the minerals of Wales—especially stone, coal, and water—were essential to it.

The Cambrian mountains reach down from Conway into the very heart of West Wales, often rising sheer out of the sea to produce a rugged and impenetrable coastline. In these mountains is a mass of rock of many, even most kinds; the hard igneous rocks abounding especially in the north. In the valleys under the hills the rugged Celts have for 2000 years fought their dual battle with nature and invaders, and Offa dug his dyke to establish their dominion. Little did the Welsh realise how important that dominion was to be in the development of the Industrial Revolution. As Thomas Telford's coast road was built towards the Lleyn Peninsula in 1826, and the Chester and Holyhead Railway followed 20 years later, it was as though each was reaching out for the materials essential to the development of the great industries of Lancashire and Yorkshire. Four great centres of the quarrying industry were to develop separately and then merge within the space of a century.

The broad estuaries of the Mersey and Dee gave Lancashire, Cheshire and Flintshire the facility to thrive as shipping centres and later to develop heavy industries. From the middle ages small sailing coasters had set out from ports along the north Wales coast to trade in these estuaries. Mainly they brought back coal, but on their outward journeys from the Conway river, Anglesey and the coastal ports around the Lleyn peninsula they needed ballast; for this they stopped under the Penmaen mountain at Llanfairfechan, where boulders of granitic rock lay in abundance on the foreshore (see Plate 27). The trade out of the Mersey and Dee multiplied and the need for stone ballast increased. There were even more rough boulders strewn over the lower slopes of the mountain, and soon the men of Penmaenmawr and neighbouring Llanfairfechan were busy making up full cargoes for the little sailing coasters, and often would arrange for the master of the next vessel to purchase the heap. They then went a step further and one or two of their number would travel with the vessel and bargain at its destination for the sale of the boulders.

For centuries, large cobble stones had been used for paving the streets of London and the centres of population in the provinces, and in the second half of the 18th century the old cobble stone pavings in London were replaced by 'causeway blocks' from Aberdeen; a new fashion in road paving developed. The men of Penmaenmawr soon realized that the stones they were shipping out could be squared and sold as setts to replace the cobbles of the industrial Midlands. From these early beginnings, partnerships of local men were formed to shape or dress selected boulders into rectangular blocks, the first crude setts. Such partnerships would hire a horse with a sledge to haul their products to the shore for shipment, for as well as setts, lump stone for building was also fashioned.

In 1820, Edward Edwards, a Conway man who was well aware of the trade in Penmaenmawr stone, made contact with Denis Brundrit of Runcorn. Brundrit owned a quarry of red sandstone at Weston Point near Runcorn and thus was already the proprietor of a few sailing vessels engaged in local coastal trading. These vessels brought ballast stone from Penmaenmawr, and Brundrit had already established a merchanting trade in it on account of its hardness. Brundrit was already in business with Philip Whiteway, a citizen of Runcorn who was also a geologist. It was Whiteway who recognised the value of the

While making repairs to the White Tower, Wren unearthed the remains of the 'Princes in the Tower', Edward and Richard. They were re-interred at Westminster Abbey.

(Above) The Library of Trinity College Cambridge and (right) The Old Ashmolean, Oxford, each built by Wren in the late 1670's.

Between 1699 and 1709, Wren rebuilt and completed the
north transept of Westminster Abbey.

The beautiful fan-vaulting above the nave of Exeter
Cathedral partly built of stone from Portland.

(Above) An early print of the King's and Queen's Baths.
(Below) The Stall Street entrance to the King's and Queen's Baths today.

(Above) Bath: The north side of Queen Square (from Jones's Views, 1829). This was the home of John Wood, built to his design in Bath stone.
(Below) Prior Park, designed by John Wood for Ralph Allen, and built entirely of stone from the Combe Down quarry. The centre block and west wing.

Prior Park, Bath: the Chapel.

(Above) The Royal Crescent, Bath. Designed and built by Wood the Younger, it was completed in 1775.
(Below) The Pump Room from Abbey Churchyard. Started by Thomas Baldwin, it was finished by John Palmer, the designer of Lansdown Crescent.

stone and learning that it came from Penmaenmawr went there to satisfy himself of its industrial and commercial possibilities.

Brundrit next met Edward Edwards at Penmaenmawr and proposed to the workers that they should sell him all the stone they collected and prepared, thereby saving them further trouble in its sale and despatch. The men were of course suspicious of losing their independence and potential gain for the future; no-one had as yet interfered with them. But Denis Brundrit was a man of determination not to be gainsaid, and in partnership with Philip Whiteway went on to obtain a lease in 1830 from the Bulkeleys of Barron Hill, Anglesey, permitting the collection of cobblestones below high watermark on the Llanfairfechan side of Penmaenmawr. The lease specified 'the getting of paving stone, squared stone, and metalling stone commonly called "Penmaenmawr paving stone",' which implied that already the stone had come to be favoured and known by this description. Brundrit also reached agreement in 1832 to collect and quarry stone on the Crown land which formed the greater part of the Penmaenmawr mountain itself. With Edward Edwards as foreman and Brundrit directing operations, business started on the existing method of converting and shipping stone taken from the lower slopes. The hauling of this stone to the ships was contracted to John Rowlands, a local farmer of Bryn Iolyn. Quarrying operations started as soon as the Crown lease was finalised and a working floor, known also as a bank or gallery, was opened in the early 1830's.

When Brundrit returned to Runcorn, Thomas Wright was sent in his place as manager in 1836. The first thing Wright did was to construct a jetty for the easier loading of ships, selecting a site under the gallery which was at an altitude of some 150 feet above the coast road that Telford had already constructed. Rail tracks were laid to connect the bank with the jetty by means of a self acting incline, the laden wagons descending counter-balancing and hauling up the empty ones. The incline was inefficient and indeed dangerous, for the winding was done by chains which used to break: soon they were replaced by wire ropes.

In time three banks came to be developed above the original one overlooking the jetty. The uppermost at a height of 500 feet resulted in the huge excavation cut into the mountainside which remains so prominent today. This floor was named Bonc Jolly,

117

after the Jolly Herring Tavern visible far below on the Bangor Road. The traveller Roscoe in 1840 wrote 'rounding the Penmaenmawr while I was tracing the sublime pass, I beheld the work of demolition in very busy progress upon the sides of the mountain. Men in every direction were blasting and breaking the masses and fragments of the giant rock, and by an ingenious contrivance, the machinery which regulated the descent of the loaded wagons along the iron rail fixed upon its almost perpendicular side, are made by a coincident action to draw up the empty carriages — continuing a perpetual ascent and descent between the magazine of broken stone and the quays of embarcation.'

The continuing call for setts in the 1830's led Samuel Holland to open the Gwylwyr quarry near Nefin on the north coast of the Lleyn peninsula. Holland also discovered rock that appeared suitable for this purpose on Eifl mountain, the most westerly of three hills known as 'the Rivals' which are familiar landmarks of great beauty a little to the northwest of Nefin. Although the landward approach to the quarry working here is gentle, to seaward Eifl mountain rises sheer out of clear water. Holland called for men from Penmaenmawr to travel the 30 miles to Trevor to test the stone for sett making and he was well pleased with the results. The original sett quarry was opened up after the fashion of Penmaenmawr, in a series of banks or levels in order to obtain sufficient length of working face. There was no road connection with the Eifl mountain and therefore shipping facilities were of the utmost importance.

In both enterprises Holland had taken a chance because at this time it had not been determined whether the proposed railway connecting London with the Dublin shipping service would operate from the coast at nearby Porth Dinllaen or at Holyhead. Plans were being considered for making Porth Dinllaen the packet station for the Dublin mail, but in the event Holyhead was selected. Undaunted, Holland pressed on with the Trevor enterprise, for the rock here proved most suitable for conversion into setts. The hardness of Trevor stone, classified as Granite Porphyry, made it ideal for use where highly polished surfaces were required, as in monumental masonry, and on rolls for calendering paper surfaces. The crushing strength and toughness of Trevor stone also made it suitable for production of stones for the winter sport of curling. It was a short step for the settmaker to prepare Trevor rock for turning, to make curling stones. A community at Trevor came into being as the quarry developed and the village was named for Holland's foreman, Trevor Jones.

While these developments were afoot at Trevor the Penmaen-mawr quarries were expanding rapidly. In 1833 a second jetty was put up on the Llanfairfechan shore and to connect the jetty with the quarry workings, an incline was laid under Telford's road. A working floor was cut in the precipitous crags overlooking the jetty at the extreme northwestern face of Penmaenmawr and this came to be known as the West Quarry. But in 1845, construction of the Chester and Holyhead Railway forced the jetty into disuse, whereas quarrying on the Penmaenmawr side of the mountain was not interfered with as the trackways there could be carried over the railway to the earlier jetty.

When the Llanfairfechan jetty was abandoned, stone from the West Quarry overlooking it had to be brought for shipment to the eastern jetty and so a trackway was cut along the 500 feet contour around the very steep face of the mountain to the point above Bonc Jolly; at first one horse did the hauling but eventually two were needed. In the end this proved to be not such a good idea, for accruing spoil or waste stone eventually blanketed all the lower banks under Bonc Jolly, and the banks themselves had to be abandoned. This was tragic, for the rock in the lower banks was of excellent quality for conversion into setts and had in many parts parallel joint planes which made the stone suitable for dressing into channels and curves, then both in great demand. All these operations had been carried out under the title of Penmaen Quarry.

A ridge of granitic rock extends eastward from the Penmaen-mawr mountain for three-quarters of a mile to the Graiglwyd mountain which is about 450 feet less in height. It is therefore not surprising that with the continuing demand for paving setts a separate undertaking soon came into production on Graiglwyd and the two undertakings developed in competition side by side. The first partners of the Graiglwyd quarry were Thomas Bracey who made his name as the great railway contractor, and John Tompkinson the builder of St. George's Hall, Liverpool. In 1836 they obtained a lease from the Brynmor Estate who claimed ownership of Graiglwyd and erected a jetty on the site of the jetty seen today. They also obtained a lease for quarrying from the Ty-Mawr estate which enabled them to carry Graiglwyd stone over Ty-Mawr land to reach the jetty.

The large rock excavation so conspicuous today, and now referred to as 'the Old Quarry' was the result of a century of quarrying of the Brynmor bank at the 1000 feet contour. The Old Quarry stone has proved to be the hardest of any stone in the United Kingdom and the most resistant to wear; it has a very fine close grain which gives a slippery surface after wear. For this reason it ceased to be worked for setts and was used for larger slabs of stone which could readily be converted to make 'wheelers'—stones which were laid as wheel tracks for carts and lorries in the sett-paved dockside areas.

Then came three 'merchants of Liverpool', Richard Kneeshaw, J. T. Raynes, and William Lupton, who were proprietors of limestone quarries at Llanddulas and already had a small fleet of coasters chiefly engaged in carrying their limestone. In 1842 this partnership took over from Bracey and Tompkinson who had done six years of pioneering work in the Graiglwyd quarry. The two rival quarry companies prospered in the early decades and the government figures for mineral statistics in the year 1858 show that Brundrit's quarries produced 50,000 tons of setts at 10 shillings per ton delivered Manchester or Liverpool, and 40,000 tons of granite building stone or 'stone floor macadam' at three shillings per ton, while the Graiglwyd quarry produced 39,000 tons of setts valued at two shillings per ton undressed and 5000 tons of granite building stone, in all making a combined output of the two quarries of 134,000 tons for that year.

The early sett makers of North Wales seemed to prefer to do their work the hard way. Whereas the Scottish and Leicestershire sett makers finished their setts in a sitting position with the sett placed before them on a powder cask filled with dirt and chips, the Welsh sett makers did their work standing up and bending over with the sett on the ground, keeping it steady under successive hammer strokes by placing the left foot against the sett. For this purpose the left boot had a metal toe-plate which was flanged upwards to protect the boot and the foot inside it. Through long years of working in this bent position many old Welsh sett makers tended to stoop 'y ddau ben yn dod ynghyd'—'the two ends coming together'. Workers then had to provide their own tools usually made for them by local or neighbouring craftsmen. Hammers and sledges were made at the local smithy, where they were forged from pieces of metal cut from old iron railings and welded on the required steel faces. Later the men had to buy from their employers tools made in Sheffield.

In the early 1850's rock-men did the double hand-drilling of bore holes necessary to receive blasting explosive, one man holding the drill while his partner struck it with a succession of blows from a five pound hammer using both hands. The rockmen had to work on ledges or 'slants' halfway up a 100 feet rock face while slung on a rope; the task needed a very good head and the man holding the drill was at considerable risk. For this work rock-men were paid by the day, a total of 15 shillings per week. When the drill hole was filled with explosives and the fuse ready to be lit, the rockmen would warn all within the danger area by shouting loudly 'War! War!', presumably an abbreviation of 'warning'. This unsatisfactory arrangement caused fatalities when workmen were out of earshot. This led to blasts taking place only at fixed hours with proper means of warning being given, so that all had time to reach protected shelter buildings. The warning of blasting was then given by a first bugle call followed after five minutes by a second call, which meant that fuses were to be lit, and after all the explosions had occurred a final 'Corn Heddwch', or peace bugle, sounded the all clear.

Single handed drillers were paid 13 shillings per week to drill and blast large rocks on the quarry floor, in readiness for 'sledgers', men who broke up the resulting lumpstone to about the size that could be lifted by hand and loaded into wagons. Each sledger was paid by the ton and had his own tally to identify his load. The end-product of this whole process was macadam, broken down by hand by the customer.

During the first three-quarters of the 19th century working hours at the quarries were long and arduous, being 12 hours a day starting at 6 am in the summer, and from dawn till dusk in winter; on Saturdays work ceased at 4 pm. Gradually the hours were reduced to 6.30 am to 5.30 pm and with a half day ending at 1 pm on Saturdays. Marshalling the loaded wagons was a great physical strain, principally because of the indifferently laid tracks high up in the quarries. The men worked at altitudes of 700 feet to over 1000 feet: only those with experience of working at such altitudes in all seasons can possibly imagine the extremes of climate in which this work took place quite normally. The men had no shelter and consequently the smithy became the canteen, for this was the only place where it was possible for a kettle to boil.

It was not unusual for quarrymen to live in Anglesey and walk to Menai Bridge station to catch an early Monday morning train, and to return home at the week-end having lodged in an over-crowded cottage. Strangely the men seemed to have been con-tented and took life philosophically. The majority held deep religious convictions which taught them to accept the ways of providence with patience and hope. They managed without the help of the Welfare State, and with a spirit of charity and comradeship were always ready to share the sorrows and burdens of others. A collection through the quarry or a chapel concert was 'eagerly patronised and never lacking'. 'Clwb-y-Jolly' was a sickness and burial club which existed as early as the 1850's and functioned right up to the introduction of the National Health Service. It was so named because early meetings were held in The Jolly Herring.

The population of the neighbouring parishes of Dwygyfylchi and Llanfairfechan grew considerably in the first half of the 19th century, the former rising from 353 to 826 and the latter from 508 to 909. There was considerable overcrowding and a number of terraced cottages were built, each comprising a living room, and a chamber or bedroom with a 'crog-loft' reached by ladder. They were sited on steep waste land and their accommodation and amenities reflected the current neglect of the working man and his family as a management responsibility. In the early 1840's any-thing approaching a substantial residence was virtually a barracks housing several families.

Railway stations were opened at Penmaenmawr in 1848 and Llanfairfechan in 1860. Immediately each gained popularity as a seaside resort which, together with increased employment at the quarries, caused a further rapid increase in population. First there was building of apartment houses (boarding houses were to come later); some of the apartment houses were imposing, being especially built to receive summer visitors. Wealthy English families were ready to pay well for accommodation, often bringing their own servants and staying for a month or more. A number of houses were also built for ambitious young sett makers and other quarrymen early in their married lives. Some of these quarrymen would collect loose stone and shape it in their leisure time to lessen the cost of building their home: there was still a plentiful supply of boulders in the sea bed at Llanfairfechan for such purposes. In this way no fewer than 24 cottages and two apartment houses were built at Llanfairfechan by quarrymen between 1860 and 1880. Mortgages were available at low rates of interest.

The market for stone was steady throughout the second half of the 19th century and only two periods of slackness are recorded. In 1868 there was a lack of trade for about nine months during which time several young men emigrated to America (hence the four 'New York Cottages' built by Brundrits at that precise time). During 1876 and 1877 a four day week was worked for some time though trade fully recovered within the period of two years. In this light it may seem strange that the Graiglwyd quarry first slackened off and then closed entirely by the mid-1870's. Kneeshaw and Lupton appear to have been more interested in a sett quarry they had taken at Port Nant near Trevor and additionally they seemed to be experiencing some difficulty with their lease of the Ty-Mawr land which at this time belonged to the Darbishire family of Pendyffryn. It is significant therefore that the Graiglwyd quarry was taken over by a partnership of members of the Darbishire family on the 1st of January, 1878. Col. C. H. Darbishire, a young man of 34, became manager and he was destined to revolutionize the quarrying industry of North Wales. He was a Civil Engineer with experience of railway construction in England and also on the Mt. Cenis railway in Italy; and he had served four years at the Penyrorsedd slate quarry where his brother was manager.

Relations with the Kneeshaw partners could not have been very good, for not only did they take away a number of their workmen to work their new quarry at Port Nant but they also made a clean sweep, transferring practically all the equipment that could be moved, including the rail, winding drums, and other gear by which the stone was taken down to the jetty and railway sliding. Furthermore the new proprietors were denied the use of the jetty at Graiglwyd as the Kneeshaw partners held this under lease from the Crown until 1887. Till then the old quarry on the Brynmor land had to remain idle, and setts were railed to Conway where they were put on board ship at Cei'r-ynys, a wharf on the junction end of the tubular bridge there. As soon as Darbishire took control he arranged a new layout whereby four inclines took the place of the previous three and additional sett banks were opened at Nant Dywyll so that by 1881 six banks existed.

It was in 1881 that Robert Footner, engineer of the London and North Western Railway, informed Col. Darbishire that it was his intention to ballast the railway track with granite, a contract which enabled Darbishire to undertake considerable expansion. The possibility of producing macadam mechanically and in greater quantity had been in Darbishire's mind, and in the same year Darbishire visited the Mountsorrel sett quarry in Leicestershire to see a stone crushing mill that had been installed there as far back as 1867; and in the following year he journeyed to Clitheroe to see a jaw-typed crusher by W. H. Baxter of Leeds, which was crushing hard limestone. Two years later Darbishire bought a Baxter machine and put it to work turning out macadam for surfacing the esplanade road then under construction at Penmaenmawr. The esplanade road was part of a scheme under which portions of the Ty-Mawr land were sold for building development, as Penmaenmawr was then growing fast as a seaside resort. Some of this land had already been mortgaged to provide capital for the development of the quarries. A portable steam engine was hired to work the crusher actually on the esplanade road site.

Five years later Darbishire sent 12 tons of lumpstone—'breakers'—to the Mountsorrel quarries to be passed through their mill. The resulting product was a guide to the type of machine that would be capable of crushing stone to the size and shape required in the macadam market. In fact the Mountsorrel plant produced a finger-shaped chip whereas a cubical shape was required. As a result a start was made in 1888 on the construction of a stone crushing mill on the 500 feet contour at a site known as Braichllwyd just below the Graiglwyd quarry on its eastern side. It was necessary for this mill to be sited close to water and a small stream was handy there; this was necessary for the steam driven engine. Also the site was level with the base, or skirts, of very large spoil heaps which had developed during 50 years of earlier quarrying. These tips of waste stone and flakings, called 'scaddlings' by the quarrymen, had been cast aside by the sett makers. This gave Darbishire material for the first 20 years opeation of the Braichllwyd mill.

The method used was conventional, whereby lumpstone passed through a crushing mill, broke up and fell by gravity through successive crushing and screening devices, falling finally into compartmented bins or hoppers, and thence sluiced into wagons running underneath the mill. The mill was primarily designed to produce ballast for the London and North Western Railway Company, but a macadam sized stone, two inches by two-and-a-half-inches, along with chippings and grit were automatically produced in the process. The mill was driven by a vertical marine type steam engine of 150 h.p. built by the de Winton Company of Caernarvon; De Winton also supplied two Lancashire type boilers 20 feet by six feet in size, and these were hauled to the site through the woods and fields of Ty-mawr by horses. As part of Darbishire's development a new jetty was opened in June 1888 and the level of the quay was raised by 25 feet, thus allowing the rail tracks on the jetty to run at a self acting gradient. As part of the project, quays were built to allow 160 railway trucks alongside them. The first train load of railway ballast left the sidings on the 15th of August, 1889.

The market was by no means confined to railway ballast however. The extension of street tramways in the second half of the 19th century called for the laying of setts between the rails and for some distance on either side of them; there was also an increase in demand for roads to be macadamized with the best possible macadam, and here the stone of the two quarries at Penmaenmawr was preferred. More hand broken macadam was being produced at the quarries, and increasing tonnages of lumpstone 'breakers' were being shipped for conversion to macadam at destination: much of this was broken up by task labour at union workhouses, and at Brundrit's own wharf at Runcorn a number of men and boys still converted the breakers into macadam. The greater portion of the Graiglwyd output was now to be de-

125

spatched by sea, for Kneeshaw's Crown lease of the jetty had lapsed in 1887. Little 'coffee-pot' locomotives, so called for their vertical boiler design, were busily engaged in running wagons along the quays, and became a familiar sight.

The Brundrit Company at the Penmaen quarry was no less active during the 1880's and 90's. A sign of the increasing scale of work in the Brundrit quarry was the introduction of the first steam locomotive, the *Mona*, which hauled stone from the West Quarry to Bonc Jolly; it is only known that she proved a failure and was quickly eliminated. In 1878 the locomotive *Penmaen* arrived from the de Winton Company of Caernarvon. The *Penmaen* gave excellent service for some 70 years working most of the time on the very exposed run around the steep face of the mountain high above the Telford Road. Moses Jones who drove her for over half a century worked in all seasons without a driver's cab. In 1888 a newer and longer jetty was constructed on the old site and the loading quays were improved. Also a stone crushing mill was constructed at Bonc Jolly designed on the lines of the Braichllwyd mill.

The Brundrit crushing mill started work in August 1893 and was fed by stones from their East Quarry which now had three banks. Two years later a fourth bank was opened and was named the Fox Bank, because a fox had often been seen there. In 1898 an even higher bank was developed, due to the continuing strength of the sett trade. This was the Kimberley Bank at a level of 1312 feet and it was so named because Kimberley was relieved in the South African War on the day it opened. Only the very summit of Penmaenmawr remained and its fate was sealed when a final floor was started above the Kimberley bank, and in time the crown of Penmaenmawr mountain was sliced off. This topmost floor was appropriately named the Attic Bank, at an altitude of 1430 feet.

The Darbishires were apparently somewhat later than the Brundrits in taking advantage of steam power for haulage. Not until 1891 did the steam locomotive *Lilian* take over the work of a horse being used for haulage on the 640 yard incline between the Braichllwyd mill and the parking sidings at sea level. Soon four similar vertical-boilered locomotives by the de Winton Company were doing duty at various sites in the quarries and these were followed by four horizontal-boilered locomotives by the Hunslet

Engine Company. Of these, one was named *Singapore*, two were named for Darbishire children and the fourth for a grandchild.

The Sett Makers Union was an early comer in the Trade Union movement and was already well established in Ireland, Scotland and in Leicestershire and other parts of England before branches were formed at the Graiglwyd and Penmaen quarries early in the 1890's. Thomas Kerswil, a Scotsman and a sett maker at Graiglwyd, was said to be the first to get his fellow workers to move in the matter. The Union's General Secretary, a Mr. Slevin, negotiated with the employers an annual 'bill of prices', that is to say, the rates to be paid for winning 10 cwts of each scale size of setts. A union minute book showed C. H. Darbishire to be a hard bargainer; he was regarded as representative of most employers in his day, though his genuine regard for his workers won him their loyalty; they usually stayed in his employment to the end of their working days. The end of the Sett Makers Union came when a Liverpool–Irish dock labourer attempted to persuade the members to join the Dockers' Union in order to demand a higher minimum wage. On reference to higher union authority, it was decreed that both unions should join the National Union of General and Municipal Workers. It took some years for ill-feelings to abate.

It seems that a Welsh surname was a bonus (if not a prerequisite) for management of both the Brundrit and Darbishire businesses. William Templeton who had been the first manager under the Kneeshaw–Raines–Lupton proprietorship and the family of McClement, a Scottish Ulsterman, were also managers under that partnership. But after that, with few exceptions, each was a Roberts, Jones, Evans, Davies, or Hughes. Brundrit's manager in the late 70's and during the 80's was known as John Jones Sol-fa because he taught with zeal the new and strange musical notation to the children at Pencae Chapel.

The changing attitude of employer to employee is illustrated in the house-building programme of the quarry owners in the last few years of the 19th century. The Darbishires built over 70 houses and several terraces on the Dwygyfylchi side of Penmaenmawr, while the Brundrit Company built slightly less in number on the Llanfairfechan side. All were beautifully built of quarried granite. The rentals were nominal to employees, being only 3s. weekly for the first decade, and when the greatly reduced scale of working came in the 20th century the houses were offered to their tenants at equally nominal figures, from £150 freehold upwards, payable by instalments.

The electrification of street tramways maintained the demand for setts until the beginning of the 20th century, but in spite of this the market for setts slowly faded as the demand for macadam, railway ballast and chippings steadily increased. The call for macadam, chippings, and grit came not only for road surfacing but also for the making of concrete; for the age of concrete had arrived.

This was the situation in 1911 when the two rival companies Brundrit and Darbishire amalgamated with the Welsh Granite Company, proprietors of the Eifl Sett Quarry at Trevor. Thus the Penmaenmawr and Welsh Granite Company Limited was formed with a capital of £434,262. One of the first developments after the amalgamation was the building of a rail link between Bonc Jolly on the Brundrit side and Braichllwyd on the Darbishire side. This was wittily christened the Canadian Pacific Railway for it symbolized peace between the two old rivals on the mountains above Penmaenmawr. The first managers of the three quarries now in partnership were A. E. Johnson at the Penmaen Quarry; H. W. Darbishire (the second son of C. H. Darbishire) at Graiglwyd, and A. H. Wheeler at the Eifl Quarry, Trevor. All looked forward with the fortitude of their predecessors, as they faced the darkening situation of the early 20th century.

13

The Reluctant Island

THE INDUSTRIAL REVOLUTION developed by both active and passive means. There were those who, taking advantage of scientific invention and rising population, brought in new industry and new methods; and there were those who seemed to stay with their former way of life but had to adjust themselves to the change that was taking place around them. Portland essentially falls into the passive category: the whole of her history is one of reaction to the events taking place around her. To understand the Portlander and his unusual outlook on life, it is necessary to look at the natural isolation of the great rock and the political experiences to which its inhabitants have been subjected in the last 900 years.

Nature intended that the Isle of Portland should be a stronghold. The approach from the north is discouraged by the Chesil Beach and by the Verne mountain which towers above Castletown harbour. Round the island shores run treacherous currents. The dangerous Race of Portland shows itself as a vast rippling of the tides called 'overfalls', caused by the unevenness of the seabed beneath it. The Race varies its position according to the direction of the wind; with a north-easterly wind it stands some two miles from the Bill and about one mile east of it; while with a south-easterly wind it is only a mile off the Bill and begins not more than three-quarters of a mile to its east. When the wind rises and the sea is high, strong tides cause it to break in great seas resembling shoal waters.

More dangerous is the Shambles, a bank of sand which lies four miles to the east of the Bill and is covered at low tide by only 12 feet of water. The Shambles extends east-north-east to west-south-west for a distance of some three miles. The Brethren of Trinity House built two lighthouses in the year 1716, one on the Bill and one in a line due north of it (the Higher Lighthouse), to give bearings to navigators by day and night to avoid these hazards. The Shambles has shifted its position through the years however, and as the position of the Race also varies with wind, there have been many groundings and wrecks through the years, and they still occur today.

But natural protection from the sea has proved insufficient for the islanders and indeed for the stronghold needed in this strategic position for the defence of England. The earliest defence in stone was Rufus Castle standing above Church Ope on the east side of the island. There is some doubt of its origin; it may have been built to the orders of William the Conqueror and completed after his death, thus being named for Rufus his son who became William II. The disastrous home rule of William II and then of his brother Henry I is well known, and led on to the chaotic period of civil war between Stephen and his cousin Matilda. During this Civil War another Rufus for whom the castle may have been named was Robert Earl of Gloucester known also as Rufus or the Red Earl. He took the castle during the Civil War when the plight of Portland and all England was gruesome and grisly.

The Anglo-Saxon Chronicle tells how the great nobles, perceiving that King Stephen was a mild, soft and good man incapable of enforcing justice, rose against him and would fight for a time on one side or the other, supporting Matilda and then Stephen. Although the nobles had done homage to Stephen they foreswore him, and the rich built castles and defended them against the King. They greatly oppressed the people by making them work in the castles and they filled them with devils and evil men. 'They stole goods by night and by day' says The Chronicle, 'seizing their owners both men and women and putting them in prison, torturing them with pains unspeakable, for never were any martyrs tormented as these were. Never was there more misery and never acted heathens worse than these . . . the earth bore no corn and you might as well have tilled the sea, for the land was all ruined by such deeds and it was said openly that Christ and his Saints slept.'

Those inhabitants of Portland who survived this reign of terror were perhaps justified in dissociating themselves with the mainland. However a connection with the mainland was vital to their existence and the first mention of Smallmouth at the east end of the Fleet, the tidal lake trapped by the Chesil Bank, appeared in the Dorset Assize roll for 1244. Here a ferry boat had connected Portland with the mainland from the very earliest times. Leland was later to describe this ferry as a 'trajectus', a boat secured to each side of the passage by a rope on which it could be pulled to and fro. It is possible that this form of tethered ferry was in use from the beginning, and it was to serve for many centuries until in 1824 an act of God made the building of the Portland Bridge a necessity.

Increasingly England's foreign policies had the effect of keeping Portland in a state of alert. During the Hundred Years War with France, Portland was always at the mercy of the enemy and 'the parish of Portland was burnt and destroyed by enemys of England, and sheep and other cattle carried away.' The islanders were already operating their quarrying rights in these early times. Stone was being moved to Exeter for the building of Exeter Cathedral early in the fourteenth century (see Plate 20). It was used for the Royal Palace at Westminster in 1347 and for repairs or extensions to the Tower of London in 1349; it was also used to build the first stone version of London Bridge in 1350.

When Henry VIII dissolved the monasteries he used part of the loot to build defences on the channel coast against the possibility of a French invasion. Among these defences was Portland Castle which guards the harbour to this day. Fifty years later, England's great sea battle against the Spanish Armada was fought in the dangerous waters around the Bill. The Spanish fleet was becalmed near the Bill on the evening of Monday 1st August, 1588 and the battle took place on the following day. Martin Frobisher, in command of the *Triumph* made use of his intimate knowledge of the treacherous seas around the Bill and anchored in the lee. From this position he was able to destroy most of the Spanish ships which were exposed not only to the English fire but to the perils of the Portland Race and Shambles Bank.

The next great trouble for Portland came with the Civil War. The islanders declared for King Charles I, the Lord of their

Manor, but in the spring of 1643 the island was cut off by land and sea and besieged by a detachment of the Parliamentary army. By early May there was 'no beere in the island nor malt to make any; there are no candels nor salt, but there is a sufficiency of other thinges, with abundance of sheepe.' Within a day or two the island and its castle were taken by the forces of Parliament. In August however Portland Castle was overrun by Royalist forces and once more the island was declared for the King: but not for long. In August 1645, the Parliamentary forces attempted to retake the Castle; the defenders held out until April 1646, by which time the Royalist cause was lost and further resistance useless. Portland was the last Royalist stronghold in Dorset to surrender.

The Rector of Portland, Dr. Humphrey Henchman was an ardent Royalist and was ejected from his benefices during the early attacks on the island, when his parsonage house and library were destroyed. Henchman was instrumental in arranging the young Prince Charles's escape from England after the Battle of Worcester in 1651, so that at the restoration in 1660, Charles rewarded Dr. Henchman by making him Bishop of Salisbury from which he was translated in 1663 to London. All this had been good for the future of Portland however, for in 1665 when Charles II had been ruling for five years, he made a grant to the inhabitants of Portland improving their return on the sale of stone in the following terms:

'Whereas our good subjects and inhabitants of our island of Portland within our county of Dorset have humbly presented to us that there are certain commons of pasture within the said Island which affords freestone in great quantities whereby the said commons are much wasted by the break of the ground and spoiled as to herbage to the great damage of the inhabitants, and that there was heretofore used to be paid the sum of 12 pence per ton for each ton of stone digged and exported out of the county, the one moiety thereof to our use as Lord of the said Island and Manor and the other to the profit of the said inhabitants; and whereas the said inhabitants have by their petitions humbly besought our royal court for the grant and confirmation of that usage and custom of the said payment of the said moiety to their use as aforesaid, We, taking the same into our consideration and calling to mind the constant loyalty and affection of the said Island to us and to our late royal father of ever glorious memory, have bethought fit to grant and we accordingly hereby declare that we have given and granted for us our heirs and successors unto our said good subjects the inhabitants of our said Island of Portland and their successors that for every ton of stone that shall be digged and taken within the said commons of that said Island except such as shall be digged and taken for our own use and services, shall be paid the sum of 12 pence, three pence whereof to be accounted to us for our use and the other nine pence to be received and retained for the sole use and benefit of the said inhabitants and their successors, and to the end that the inhabitants may certainly know what shares so taken is for us and we do hereby grant and declare that no stone shall be taken for our use, save only such as shall be digged there and carried thence under the hand and seal of our surveyor of our works for the time being expressing the same to be for our particular service, and our will and pleasure is that this our gracious grant and declaration be entered and registered in the rolls of the court of the said inhabitants, there to remain upon record as our royal consolation and settled agreement in this matter. Whereof all our officers and ministers and all others our subjects whom it may concern are to take due notice. Given at our court at Oxford under our signet and sign manuell, the third day of November in the 17th year of our reign, 1665.'

It must be remembered that Charles II was already much concerned with the state of St. Paul's Cathedral in London at this time although he could not know that the Great Fire would come in the following year. It is clear therefore that Charles was expressing genuine gratitude to the islanders of Portland for the great support they had given to the Royal court during the Civil War. The islanders now had new cause to retain and guard their ancient rights by which every tenant had raised what stone he pleased in his own respective tenament provided he did not hurt the highways and paid the customary duty to the Crown.

During the second half of the 17th century it is possible to see the bigger quarry operator coming into existence, and this was

133

perhaps inevitible due to the greater calls for stone following the Fire of London and the need for equipment and labour on a considerable scale. The first name to emerge as a substantial operator was that of Thomas Gilbert, a native of the Island of Portland, with whom the committee of St. Paul's contracted in 1698 for the supply of stone and for the building of a roadway to connect the quarries with the pier. Gilbert was a member of The London Mason's Company, and was the largest purveyor of Portland stone in London. Later, in 1700, Christopher Wren gave Thomas Gilbert then overseer of His Majesty's Quarries in the Island of Portland an order to raise 2000 tons of Portland stone 'of such scantlings as shall be directed by commissioner Greenbill for the use of His Majesty's Docks at Portsmouth.' (See Fig. 6 page 228.)

When Thomas Gilbert and his wife died in 1704 and 1705, their executor Edward Tucker of Weymouth went on to dominate the industry in the new century. Tucker was one of the Members of Parliament for Weymouth and in 1717 he succeeded Sir Christopher Wren as Surveyor of the Quarries on the island. Edward had two sons and a daughter; John succeeded his father as a Member for Weymouth and Richard as Surveyor of the Quarries. Their sister Rebecca who had married Gabriel Steward outlived her brothers. In 1788 Gabriel was appointed by the Crown as Lieutenant of the Island and Governor of Portland Castle, besides being a Member for Weymouth and Mayor of Weymouth in 1769 and 1779. Their children took the name of Tucker-Steward and the first son, also Gabriel, continued the family business. He carried on the tradition of the family, for he too was a Member for Weymouth and Mayor of the town in 1790 and 1800; and in 1791 succeeded his father as Lieutenant and Governor of the Castle. In this way the Tuckers and the Stewards dominated the Island, and with it the Portland stone industry, throughout the 18th century and into the early 19th century too.

The trading in the 18th century was not without its risks. The ship *Dorothy* loaded with stone and bound for Dublin was the victim of a late Spanish success in the English Channel where she was boarded and captured by an unnamed vessel. More amusing was the quandary of the Tucker family when a sloop bearing Portland stone for Matthew Elliott, a stone merchant in Canterbury, ran aground off Beachy Head and proved impossible to salvage. The Tuckers wrote to Mr. Ambrose Galloway, a stone merchant of Lewes, asking him to find someone to salvage the cargo. A long dispute followed as to whether Matthew Elliott the stone merchant of Canterbury should pay any part of the costs which he had refused to do. Said Elliott: 'Sr. I am in formed that James Dyer was Dronk at ye time that he Lost your Vessill neather had he hands on Bord that was Capable of doing aney thing without his a Sistance . . . after ye Vessill strok ye man was trobeled to wake Dyer he was so Dronk'.

Then came the French Revolution and Portland was once more under a continuing threat of war. William Morton Pitt, a member of Parliament for the county, made a survey of the coast of Dorsetshire for the purposes of planning a scheme of defence in the year 1798. His manuscript report emphasizes that 'should an enemy get possession of the Island of Portland with a sufficient store of provision, serious consequences might ensue; its defence and that of Weymouth are therefore objects of national importance'. John Penn (grandson of William Penn who had been given Pennsylvania to develop, as the settlement of a debt with King Charles II) was now Lieutenant and Governor of Portland Castle; he raised and commanded the Royal Portland Legion, a volunteer force for the defence of the island. This unit was also known as 'the Coast Fencibles', and one of Upham's paintings shows a review of the Legion in Park Field where John Penn and King George are pictured together on horseback. Yet a third name for the island legion was the Portland Volunteers; John Penn was Captain with Henry Lowman as Lieutenant.

This was apparently not enough, for in 1803 the frigate *Aigle* stood off Chiswell and Captain George Woolf came ashore with a press gang. After capturing two men at Chiswell they went on to Easton, but a large number of Portlanders resisted them; in the scuffle that ensued the press gang opened fire killing three Portlanders of whom two, Alexander Andrews and Richard Flann, were quarrymen and the third a blacksmith. The Captain's account of the incident differed vastly from that of the Portlanders and in a lawsuit that followed the coroner declared a verdict of wilful murder against Captain Woolf, Lieutenant Francis Hastings, Lieutenant Jeffries of the marines, and Mr. John Fortiscue Morgan a midshipman, who were all lodged in Dorchester gaol.

Despite the efforts of the Portlanders, who used the Stone Grant Fund to provide for their legal costs, the accused were acquitted by jury at the Summer Assizes in Dorchester on the grounds that they had acted in self-defence.

There are contradictory estimates of the volume of export tonnage of Portland stone at the beginning of the 19th century, but the figure can be put between 20,000 and 30,000 tons per annum. An estimate that 800 men and boys, 180 horses, and 50 ships were engaged in the stone trade is dubious, for the total population of the island was then just over 2000. And when in 1839 Commissioners were appointed by Parliament to consider what stone should be used in building the new Houses of Parliament the annual production of all the quarries in the Island was still about 24,000 tons, coming from 56 quarries, but only 240 quarrymen were continually employed, 138 of them working for Stewards. The lot of the 180 horses was not a happy one. The Rev. J. Skinner, Rector of Camerton near Bath, when visiting Portland in September 1804 wrote:

'Large hewn stones lie scattered in all directions; indeed the quarries worked on the island are prodigious; and the mode of conveying the ponderous masses down the steep unavoidably arrests the attention of the stranger. The blocks being placed on a strong wooden carriage, with solid wheels proportionate to the weight they are to sustain, two horses are harnessed one before and sometimes two behind; the latter being supplied with strong breeching, in order to act as drawbacks to the carriage and prevent it running with too great velocity down the steep (see Plate 5).

'Indeed the exertions of these poor animals in this arduous employment is really astonishing; they squat down on their haunches, and suffer themselves to be dragged for many yards, struggling with all their strength against the weight that forces them forwards. To one unaccustomed to the sight, it appears as though their limbs must inevitably be dislocated or their sinews cracked by the violence of their exertions: indeed one compassionates these poor creatures the rather, as all this labour might easily be obviated by a simple construction of a railroad. Why this has not been long since performed is to me surprising and especially as Portland stone is in universal request'.

The comments of the reverend gentleman were prophetic for the Merchants' Railway was to be constructed some 30 years later.

In the next 50 years things were to move very fast in Portland for its importance strategically was gaining rapidly. The French were engaged in preparing a massive fortified harbour for their fleet at Cherbourg, and this caused the Navy to select Dover, Seaford and Portland as fortifications to counter this threat to the English coast; furthermore the size of ships of the British Navy was increasing so that they could no longer enter the smaller ports and a deep water refuge was becoming a necessity. In 1826 a Bill was prepared for the construction of a breakwater in Portland Roads. A Royal Commission was set up and held the opinion that 'there is everything at Portland to render the construction of a breakwater easy, cheap, and expeditious, and the holding ground in the Roads is particularly good. A large part of the island facing the bay is Crown property, and contains abundance of stone. It has numerous springs and plenty of the best water may be led in any direction for the supply of ships. The island of Portland possesses great natural advantages for defence, and for the formation of a naval and military depot during war to any extent that may be required'. It was another 20 years however before the Commission's recommendations led to the construction of the breakwater.

For Portlanders to remember a storm, it has to be no less than a hurricane: such was the Great Gale of 1824. This November gale did vast damage, drowning 26 people and destroying 100 houses (because of the complicated law of inheritance on the island the houses were never rebuilt). A contemporary account says: 'the Ferry House at Smallmouth was precipitated by the violence of the winds into a heap of ruins; the poor honest worthy old ferryman after 30 years service in that capacity fell a victim to his benevolence and humanity in a noble and generous attempt to preserve the life of a dragoon: he was carried away by the force and impetuosity of the current and inevitably lost. The Chisel Bank throughout its whole extent was lowered from 20 to 30 feet.' A temporary ferry was re-established, and by ancient decree, tolls continued to accrue to the Lord of the Manor. An Act of 1835 empowered the building of a toll bridge and at last, in January 1839 there was safe and permanent access to the Island.

On the 10th June 1825, Royal Assent was given to an Act of Parliament authorising 'the making and maintenance of a railway or tram road in the Parish of St. George in the Island of Portland in the county of Dorset to be known as The Portland Railway Company' (see Plates 28 and 29). The railway was not to interfere with or impede the military defence of Portland Castle and no building was to be erected within 200 yards of it. No time was lost and in October 1826 the 'Merchants' Railway', as it was to be known, came into service. It had been designed to ease the transport of stone from the quarries down to Castletown for shipment by sea, and it was the very first railway of any type built in this part of the country. The railway was always horse-drawn, and the tracks ran from the vicinity of Priory Corner around above Fortuneswell to a point high above Castletown. Thence the stone was lowered down the incline on cables, the full wagons being used to pull empty ones up as they descended.

The 16 proprietors of the Merchants' Railway were all quarry owners five being members of the Tucker Steward family. Between them they had subscribed £5000 against an estimated cost of £4689 12s., so permission was readily granted. Rates were laid down under the Act for the carriage of stone, the best not exceeding 8d. per ton per mile, and 'roach stone, cappings, ashlars for building, limestone, and all other inferior stone, not exceeding 6d. per ton per mile. The Railway at harbour level crossed the Parish Road to the west of the Jolly Sailor Beer House, and divided to 11 separate branches at the piers. The owners of the loading stations included Stewards (Nos 1 and 2), Wm White, Weston (Nos 5, 8, and 11), Richardson and Weston, Weston and Lang, Dike, Robert Stone and Comben. The Merchants' Railway was to run for over a 100 years, finally discontinuing in 1939.

The Breakwater Act of 1847 provided not only for the building of the breakwater which effectively made a naval harbour, but for a military fortification to be built on the Verne overlooking the harbour and thus protecting the shipping there, and for a prison. It also empowered the Commissioners of Her Majesty's Woods to purchase the necessary land. As the inhabitants and tenants had ancient rights on the common land of the Verne, much discussion took place with a view to reasonable compensation being given to the Portlanders for their loss of rights.

A considerable amount of common land was required, for the Verne was the dominating site needed for the military fortification and for the prison that was to supply cheap labour (see Plate 30). Possibly in anticipation of the legal wrangles that were to follow, the customs and privileges of the Island and Royal Manor of Portland were reaffirmed at a Court of Survey held between the 20th May and the 7th July, 1846. The various 'presentments' by which the privileges are stated concluded thus: 'And we lastly Present and say, that we have no written customary to produce beyond the Presentments from time to time recorded in our Court Books, and we continue all former and other general Presentments in the said Books which are now applicable and in force.' The Court Leet clearly did not intend to arbitrate for the Islanders, but a Committee, including John Stone, the Crown Steward, and Benjamin Pearce, the Agent, was formed for the purpose.

In 1847 this committee agreed to a figure of £20,000 as suitable compensation. A proposal that half the sum of £20,000 be divided amongst the islanders proportionately to the quit rent paid by them was readily accepted; but proposals for disposing of the remaining £10,000 led to such acrimony that a further Act of Parliament to amend the first Act and 'to make further provision for the division and application of the purchase money' received royal assent in the summer of 1850. Generally the £10,000 was divided between a better water supply, an investment in the Royal Portland Dispensary, the paying off of tolls on the Ferry Bridge and 'the provision and endowment of schools and school buildings and teachers' for the education of the children of the inhabitants. Argument continued to rage in Portland for some time after the Act had settled the matter finally. Meanwhile the Breakwater had been under construction for four years.

It is not always appreciated that Portland Prison was not envisaged merely to provide cheap labour for the construction of the breakwaters and other defence works on the Island. It was also an important experiment in dealing with men sentenced to transportation under a new scheme whereby they could earn a 'ticket of leave' during a year spent in a closed prison in England. This was a reward for good behaviour and after transportation they could enjoy a considerable amount of freedom. Attempts were made to give the convicts some education and to teach them a useful trade. In 1848, 206 men had been sent from other prisons to Port Philip at Sydney, New South Wales, and 35 to Moreton Bay, and of these only 26 were sent back for further confinement. Portland Prison was completed within a year, and the first detachment of 54 convicts arrived at Portland in November 1848 aboard HMS *Driver*. In 1851, 862 prisoners were received at Portland, and 819 embarked for transportation, mostly to Western Australia. In that year two men escaped from the prison, and from that time sentries were posted at Ferry Bridge during prison working hours.

The average number of convicts at Portland was about 1500, against which some 700 were employed in the quarries and 450 in dressing and squaring stones for the Breakwater. In 1849 Prince Albert laid the foundation stone of the first breakwater, and into the stone was deposited a set of the current coins of the realm, covered by a plate bearing the inscription 'on the 25th day of July 1849 in the 12th year of the reign of Her Most Gracious Majesty Queen Victoria his Royal Highness Prince Albert KG, KCB, KCM deposited this stone to record the commencement of the Portland breakwater. James Meadows Rendel engineer-in-chief, John Coode resident engineer.' Within a few years the breakwaters, military fortification, and barracks for the officers were all completed.

The introduction of modern local government to Portland was yet another somewhat stormy affair. The Local Government Act of 1858 was first adopted at a public meeting on Portland held on the 18th January 1866. But on 16th February 1867 a petition was sent to the Home Secretary opposing this first adoption. A public enquiry was held on 29th March 1867 and in April the Local Government Act of 1858 was finally adopted. This brought into existence the Portland Local Board of Health, which later became the Portland Urban Sanitary Authority. The Portland Urban District Council was formed on January 1st 1895 and was to serve until March 31st 1974.

The harnessing of steam power brought mechanization to the quarries in the mid-19th century. At first came steam winches in the quarries (see Plate 31) and stone working machinery of a primitive type for cutting the quarry blocks into sawn slabs; and later came planing machines for moulding the slabs. Gradually the individual Portlander's stone rights were being taken up and merged into a recognisable industry by a few commercial groups of which the Stone Working and Quarrying Company Limited and the Portland Stone Company Limited were two; in 1891 these merged under the proprietorship of F. J. Barnes. The detail of sorting out the shares in the feudal furlongs that were acquired in the long process of consolidation gave—and continues to give—the quarry managers an endless task; for the holdings of the tenants are to this day handed down 'undivided'. The principle of converting family rights into limited company shares seems to have had no appeal, though it would have eliminated the need to deal in terms of 'the quarter of the third part of half an acre.'

In all this history, the one constant factor is the reluctance of the Portlanders to accept change, which has resulted in a continuous rear-guard action against progress. Although the islanders will readily concede that Portland is 'a fine place for women and cats but a hell of a place for men and horses' they love it yet and resent with a deeply ingrained thoroughness the intrusion of Kimberlins and the march of progress from the mainland. In a census of 1851 only one girl on the island braved 'Victoria' as a christian name.

14

---·❀·---

Man Into Stone

T HE STONE INDUSTRY of Wiltshire was finally forced into greater activity by the processes of the Industrial Revolution. The market for Bath stone was progressively opened up by the Avon Navigation, the Avon-Kennet Canal, and the Great Western Railway. Though stone output increased enormously as a result, this did not immediately transform production methods: the mining of stone under Box Hill and Corsham was developed in a primitive and arduous manner. The important thing, it seems in retrospect, was the quality and quantity of superb limestone that these hills in Wiltshire had to offer, once the existence of the stone was discovered.

The Bristol Avon rises high in the Cotswolds and curls clockwise down the valley separating them from the White Horse Hills. When it reaches Bradford-on-Avon, the river turns west to Bath through the gorge separating the Cotswolds from the Mendips. Around Bath the Jurassic beds are tilted in a gently inclined plain sloping south-eastward, and here may be found a great variety of limestones, sandstones and clays. Much of England's best building stone lies in these hills. Geologically (and logically) stones are described from the youngest beds at the surface to the oldest at the base, and hence the Jurassic formations are categorized as:

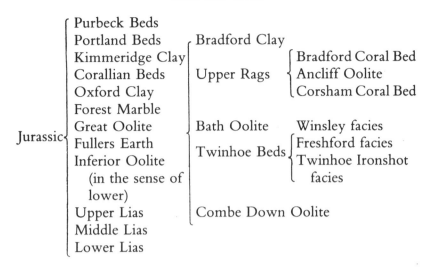

All the Bath stones belong to the Great Oolite: south of the Avon they lie high in the hills, but often close enough to the surface to be obtained by opencast quarrying, as for example at Combe Down and Odd Down. Exposures in the hills on both sides of the Avon valley were quarried in early times by the Romans and their successors. North of the river, in the foothills of the Cotswolds, the rock beds under the hilltop capping mostly lie deeper beneath the surface; to reach the qualities of stone required for building purposes it is necessary to mine, as at Box, Corsham, Conkwell, Monkton Farleigh and Winsley. The overlying sequence of Bradford clay in the succession of geological strata here is of great importance to the mining industry, for this layer acts as a waterproofing horizon for the mines below. As water descends from the surface it is diverted through the rocks along the top of the impervious clay bed, so keeping the mines relatively dry.

Though at law there has always been much confusion between the terms 'quarry' and 'mine' it has been customary in the stone industry to refer to all activities as quarrying operations; however, the difference remains. Quarries are normally approached by adits—horizontal or inclined passages—which either run into the side of a cliff (in the case of Clift and Nobels' quarries the result of earlier activities), or they may run under an archway and along a cutting as at Strong's Quarry and the Lower Hill Quarries. On the other hand mines must be approached either by vertical or sloping shafts, and the supreme example of vertical shaft entry is to the quarry known as the Cathedral, worked between 1830 and 1850 (see Plate 32). Here the stone was chiselled out, and worked downwards with galleries driven off at three levels to find the good stone. The Cathedral is some 100 ft. deep, 200 ft. long, and 25 ft. wide narrowing to a passage at each end; the stone was winched up through a sharp hole in the roof. The sloping shaft was used for quarries opened in the Corsham area; they usually slope at an angle of 45° and require some 200 steps for descent to the average level of 90 ft. below the surface where the best beds are found. At this level the temperature remains at 11.1°C (52°F) throughout the year.

Although the quarrying industry was continuous from the days of the Romans right up to the 19th century, the scale of work was not great; buildings of the quality of Malmsbury Abbey in the eighth century, Lacock Abbey in the 13th century and Longleat House in the 15th century were built of Bath stone (see Plates 33 and 34), won from the hill quarries manually and often under awesome conditions. But the mining of stone was to come later and derived from one of the earlier developments of the Industrial Revolution affecting the West Country. Ralph Allen perhaps had a better concept of the new world offered by the Industrial Revolution than most of his contemporaries; for he rapidly took advantage of the Avon navigation to Bristol and he would have welcomed the Avon-Kennet Canal, opened in 1810, had it been built when it was first mooted, in his lifetime, and the railways that were to follow.

For it was railway development that brought home to the quarrymen of Wiltshire the true value of the stone that lay hidden under the Cotswolds. In 1833 Isambard Kingdom Brunel, a young man of 24, was appointed Engineer of the newly-formed Great Western Railway. Brunel was the son of a famous engineer who had constructed Woolwich Arsenal, Chatham Dockyard, and the Thames Tunnel. Young Brunel was to become even more famous, and his engineering skill and his ability to improvise were unique in their day. The Cotswolds stood across the path of the railway that was to link Bristol with London and there was no means by which the construction of a tunnel could be avoided.

So far, the course of the railway had been selected in such a way as to concentrate gradients and tunnels as much as possible but Box Hill, lying equidistant from Chippenham and Bath was a challenge in every sense of the word: for under the hill lay the long, hard, oolite reef. The hill towered 400 ft. above the level of the railway and thus it was impractical if not impossible to cut an open gorge or ravine through the hill; indeed, the boring of a tunnel was at first deemed to be equally impossible. However work on the tunnel started with the sinking of a trial shaft in 1836 and in that year a contract was let for the sinking of six permanent shafts and two temporary ones each of 28 ft. diameter. A contractor named Horton undertook the construction of the shafts at the Corsham and Box ends of the tunnel but failed to complete the work. It took two years for his successors to complete all the shafts which varied from 70 to 300 ft. in depth.

The Directors of the Great Western Railway were concerned with rumours which circulated to the effect that the tunnel project was impossible and in February 1837 declared that 'unfounded reports were circulated industriously during the first application to Parliament respecting imaginary difficulties to be encountered in the tunnel through Box Hill, east of Bath. It may be a satisfaction to the proprietors to know that a trial shaft has been sunk and the strata through which it passes fully ascertained; the result of which not only proves the incorrectness of such reports, but gives full assurance of the work being free of all expected difficulties. The completion of the permanent shafts is now far advanced and the work on the tunnel will be commenced as quickly as possible'. All were sunk by the autumn of 1837 and tenders for the tunnel itself were then invited.

Contracts were let and plans were made for the tunnel to be completed in a matter of 13 months ending in August 1840, the work being in charge of William Glennie, one of Brunel's assistants who was resident engineer. Contracts with Mr. Lewis of Bath and Mr. Brewer of Box required that they commenced operations at opposite ends of the tunnel, and when they had worked towards the centre there was great anxiety as to whether they should have kept to a straight line producing a true union of the tunnel headings; but when the intervening portion of rock was removed the accuracy of the headings was incredible. The junction of the two roofs formed an unvarying line and was perfect 'to a hair'; while the sides were so true that the utmost deviation from a straight line was less than one-and-a-half inches.

George Burge, a Herne Bay businessman who had contracted to construct the St. Catherine Docks in London, was to be responsible for lining the tunnel with brickwork, and thirty million bricks were used in the process. The bricks or most of them were made by a Mr. Hunt in kilns to the west of Chippenham: Hunt employed a hundred horses and carts for three years to carry them. From the east end of the tunnel the excavators encountered the rock strata in succession from Great Oolite or Bath stone, through a thick bed of light coloured clay or fullers earth to Inferior or Lower Oolite, and then to Blue Marl and finally Lias, all sloping from west to east at a steep angle to the tunnel. The tunnel itself was driven on a gradient of 1:153 ft. to the mile, running downhill to the west.

During the two and a half years of excavation, one ton of gunpowder and one ton of candles were consumed each week in blasting and lighting operations. The fears of a party of directors of the Great Western Railway may be imagined when they consented to be lowered down one of the shafts with Brunel during a visit to the tunnelling operations. While suspended some 150 ft. from the tunnel level and tipping around in a greasy muddy tub with little light, their feelings of insecurity were increased manifold as blasting started up in the operations below them and vibrated through the long drawn caverns.

Difficulties of blasting through the rock were by no means the only ones encountered by Lewis and Brewer. There was a constant flow of water into the works through numerous fissures in the rock during the rainy season, and at times this was so formidable as 'almost to destroy hope of completing it'. In November 1837 the steam pump then employed was inadequate to the task of making headway against the flow of water; the volume increased and filled the tunnel rising to a height of 56 ft. in the shafts. This caused a total suspension of work until the following July. Even this did not discourage the contractors from forging on with their work. Although the tunnel was flooded again in November 1838, stopping operations for 10 days, the tunnel was completed with the help of an additional pump worked by a steam engine of 50 h.p. Apart from the steam powered pumps everything was achieved by man, horse, gun-powder and gravity. Some 300 horses were used in relays in the tunnelling operation, and there were about 40 boys to drive them. Between 1100 and 1200 men did the manual work for Burge alone, and for most of the time work went on round the clock. During the last six months the labour force increased to 4000.

June 30th 1841 was the final date of opening of Box tunnel for commercial traffic. A single line of the broad seven foot gauge rail was ready, and during the first three days Daniel Gooch, locomotive superintendent of the Great Western Railway himself acted as pilot with every train. The first train was one for the general public leaving Bristol at 7 am for London. However a train decorated with flags and bearing the directors and executive of the Great Western Railway left Paddington at 8 am and this is usually referred to as the first train to pass through the tunnel.

The darkness of the tunnel struck terror into the hearts of the public and a scheme to pacify them by lighting the tunnel was attempted but rapidly abandoned. Brunel in a report said 'I am afraid there are no means of remedying the evil of darkness in tunnels unless by a brilliant illumination which would of course be very costly. The extent of evil however is this, that the tunnel is during 24 hours as dark as the rest of the line frequently is during the night, but is otherwise exposed to fewer casualties.' In March 1845 and again some 50 years later severe frosts caused scaling and brought down stone onto the track. The second fall resulted in further brick lining and arching of the tunnel, which had previously been considered unnecessary.

The work of construction was not without casualties; about 100 men were killed in different parts of the works and a larger number injured. Twenty six inspectors were employed to supervise the project and a number of the inspectors were sent to different villages to keep the peace on Sundays; or at least to attempt to do so, for there were no county police at that time. Most of the workmen were housed in Box and Corsham villages, and as gangs worked round the clock, their beds were never cold. Drunkenness and fighting were very common and teetotalism among the working class in those days was practically unheard of.

It was Brunel's tunnel that drew the attention of the stone industry to the volume and quality of stone lying under the hills to the east of the City of Bath. The tunnel revealed the secret: the railway itself supplied the means of transporting the stone: and nature herself provided the conditions for a classic example of economic mining. The natural dipping of the oolite stone beds reached the precise level of the railway line near the eastern end of the tunnel. As the quarrymen developed a network of railway lines underground reaching far into the stone galleries, it thus became possible to use gravity to feed the loaded wagons down to the railway station at Corsham.

Although the canal system and later the railway system did much to accelerate the Industrial Revolution, neither did much to encourage the stone trade in the West Country to take advantage of power and mechanization. As the tonnage of stone taken out of the mines beneath Box Hill grew—by 1864 this had reached a figure of 2000 tons per week leaving Corsham station (see Plate 35)—quarrying was still carried out by the old arduous method, and in fact it was to be another 94 years before the mining operation was fully mechanized.

The essential difference between mining for stone and for other minerals is in the handling of the product, which in the case of stone must be done with great care. No explosives or drastic methods of winning the stone may be employed. Hence it follows that the methods of miners at the working face must be slow and manual. Working into the stone from a frontal position, a roadway or tunnel is continuously driven into the rock as they progress. The width of the face and hence of the tunnel usually averages about 10 feet which is a convenient width for the stone to be divided laterally into three blocks. The old method, often called the ancient method (see Plates 35, 36, 37 and 38), started with the miner marking a line horizontally across the face of the heading some six to nine inches down from the roof and the first stage was to chip away the stone from roof level down to this horizontal mark. This work was extremely tiring and difficult and required great skill; of all the work in the mines it was the most disliked among the miners. The picking of this stone was done with hand picks to a depth of five feet back from the stone face. It has been said that the 'picker' skilled with his pick could hit a fly at the back of the five-foot crevice. The picker used both hands to 'throw' the pick at the back of the crevice and in the course of this

148

North side of
the Bath Street
colonnade,
designed by
Thomas Baldwin.

The Thames barge *May*, often sailed between Portland and the Thames with cargoes of Portland stone. Her first regular trip was in 1891 and her last in 1933. But in 1972 she made a special trip to help St Paul's Restoration Fund.

The quarries at Penmaenmawr, Gwynedd, where the
North Wales sett industry began early in the 19th Century.

(Above) A 19th Century drawing of Portland, showing the causeway flanked by the short-lived railway to the Island on the left, and Chesil Beach on the right.

(Below) The Merchants' Railway, Portland, was built in fifteen months and came into service in 1826. For over a hundred years this horse-drawn railway served the Island's quarrymen.

The Merchants' Railway; the point may be seen where laden and
empty wagons were able to pass on the self-acting incline.

(Above) A view rising up to The Verne, Portland, taken from the east coast quarries.
(Below) Looking into the evening sun above Fortuneswell. Chesil Beach stretches north-west to Bridport, and Weymouth may be discerned in the north-east.

Lifting out a broken hand crane, circa 1893.

(Above) 'The Cathedral'. An example of the vertical shaft entry. Galleries were driven off at different levels to find good stone.
(Below) Sloping shaft at Monks Park. In the early days horses were used to wind the load to the surface.

movement had to let go with one hand, being cramped for space. The recess tapers from a depth of about nine inches at the front to a mere four inches at the back.

When this recess had been made, a sawyer next used saws to cut in vertically at right angles to the face; the saws were heavy, being six or seven feet in length with names like 'bacon-slasher' and 'frig-bob', according to use. They were long enough to reach to the back of the crevice with some to spare, and with them the face was cut into three or more sections depending on the face width. The sawyer would sit and rock backwards and forwards on a mushroom-like one-legged stool to complete the sawing operation. After the vertical cuts were made the 'wrist' was next removed; this was (and is) usually the block of stone on the left side of the face, and removal was accomplished by splitting the block off the rock at its base using 'chips and wedges'. Picks or chisels were used to cut pockets a few inches in depth along the base of the wrist and into each of these pockets, two chips with rounded faces were inserted, and between them a wedge driven. The block would then split off along the plane of its natural bed at the base, and at the same time the back would crack at some point along the depth of the crevice; with luck it might crack at the very back of the crevice; but sometimes it would crack halfway or even less from the front, in which case chips and wedges were again used to free the back part.

The block thus freed was next removed using a lewis bolt, a long bolt (with an eye for lifting at one end and a nut on the other) onto which three pieces of metal are threaded, the outer pieces flanging outwards and the centre piece being straight. The lewis bolt was certainly in use in medieval times, and is still used today in some mines. A hole of conical shape is cut into the top of the stone to be lifted, and the two flanged pieces of metal are fitted into the cone: the centre piece is next placed between them, locking them into the cone. The long bolt is then threaded through the three pieces and held by the nut. Finally a chain is attached to the lifting eye and the block is hauled away by crane. Chock holes about one inch square may still be seen in the roof of the quarry network where the main pillar of the wooden crane, adjustable in height, was screwed between roof and floor to achieve strength and rigidity.

Once the wrist had been removed, there was access to the back of the other two blocks, which could be sawn vertically, parallel with the face, starting with special saws known as 'razzers'; these were five or six feet long tapering from six inches in depth at the handle to barely one inch at the tip. Razzers were used to cut down the first 12 inches from the picking crevice. Thereafter larger saws seven feet in length and 10 inches in depth were used to cut right down to the rock bed. Then chips and wedges were again used to separate the block at the foot of the face.

When the blocks were lifted clear the miner satisfied himself that each block was sound in every way. The block would therefore be 'sounded' for defects such as cracks which could be disastrous at a later stage in finishing the stone, or by faults lying within the block itself. These were—and still are—detected by tapping the stone and listening for its ring. The sound block of stone will ring true when tapped, but if faulty will only respond with a dull thud. The skilled miner will know instantly whether a fault of one kind or another exists, and will track it down and where necessary divide the block so that what is good is finally retained at its maximum size, in one or more pieces. Miners have individual preferences for tapping instruments, some using metal bars, some using other rock from the quarry, and some even a pebble from the seashore. They say: 'sound rocks yield large blocks'. Early in the 20th century blocks up to eight tons in weight were taken, but now the maximum is five tons.

In the earliest times the hauling away of stone was done by horses, but in the 19th century this gave way to trucks hauled by diesel shunters in the adits, and to steam-powered winding where the stone had to be hauled up a slope or vertical-shaft. The freestones of Bath cannot be taken directly from the mine in winter because their moisture makes them vulnerable to frost action; the stone is therefore stored in worked-out headings to dry out before being brought to the surface. In summer, when this risk does not exist, the stone may go straight out into the open air, but is still better for a short period of maturation before shipment. When different headings ran parallel to each other, it was possible to take out part of the stone dividing them leaving only a series of unhewn pillars to support the roof, at the same time providing storage space between them. The hard ragstone capping bed in the roof of the mines is so good that it is very rare for props to be needed to prevent falls, and these natural pillars can stand as far as 25 to 30 feet apart.

Prior to stacking either underground or on the surface the quarried blocks are trimmed or 'scappled' by saw, axe, or adze to make them into shapes and sizes capable of easy handling in the masonry works. This work is carried out by 'choppers' who chop off the rough faces of the natural beds to make the stones square and even. After this the cubic content of each block is marked on one side with a 'scriber' together with a number from series allocated to the individual quarries for reference purposes. It is normal practice to scribe a line on the face of a block from one bed to another thus enabling the stone merchant to see at a glance which is the natural bed of the stone, for without the line this might not be easy to discern in a seasoned block. Scribing is even more essential when dealing with stone other than freestone which must always be erected permanently on its natural bed.

For lighting, disused saw-sharpening files were hammered into the walls at intervals in the galleries as brackets for hanging lights; alternately little niches were sometimes cut into the pillars, and here lamps have often left traces of soot. Stone benches may be seen in the mines with heaps of old files nearby, relics of a near-forgotten era. Here saws were inserted upside down into a cut in the bench leaving the miner with both hands free to sharpen them.

The conditions under which the quarrymen worked in the mines were hard, but the men were highly religious and accepted their fate with resignation. Years ago when a licence was required for preaching in certain buildings, the old quarrymen used to congregate underground on a Sunday morning and hold their service in a gallery, with one of their number acting as lay preacher; the particular gallery they selected is still known as Chapel Ground. The walls of Great Oolite offered considerable opportunities for graffiti and the quarrymen were prolific in this regard. It must be said however that well over half the surviving messages and quotations engraved on the gallery walls are religious, and none of the others are particularly crude. 'Want these two cut to size at once—1/4.8 × 1.6 × 2.0 and 1/4.8 × 1.8 × 2.6' was engraved in a slower age which lacked the simple appurtenances of administration; 'S. Milsom is a dry old stick' is happily anonymous; 'John Cox had not any tobaco to give away' has a timeless ring; and 'October 6th, 1887 Salvation Army heard at Chippenham' was a rewarding day for General Booth. The Salvation Army was not yet 10 years old.

There were several families who each contributed many members to the stone industry under Box Hill; the Barnets had no less than 16 sons, grandsons and great grandsons working in the mines in the 19th century and the Danceys had 13; there were eight Pinnocks, five Hiscocks, four Dykes and four Lights. They were brought up to believe in stone and to be happy working to win it. They were strong men with little patience for difficulties. When Herbert Tinson, a distaff son of the Dancey family suffered a collapsed wheel to his barrow his father's comment was 'get on with it—its only one wheel'; with that good advice Herbert Tinson forsook the quarrying business and sensibly married the daughter of the landlord of the Quarrymen's Arms, and so in turn came to be its landlord.

Jack Dancey, now over 80 years old and living on the brow of Box Hill, has only one regret: that he is not half his age. His favourite story is of old Fred Robbins, a haulier of stone so mean that his horses used to drop dead in the traces. Jack worked for him haymaking, and when it came to payment Robbins had a stock answer: 'I don't know how to pay 'ee Jack; a penny is too little and a penny ha'penny too much. I wish I hadn't taken 'ee on.' Jack Dancey shows few marks of the long hard life he spent under the Avon hills; in all but his last ten years Dancey pursued the ancient method of winning the stone: mechanization did not reach the mines until 1948.

The updating of method in the Wiltshire mines was a matter of economics, for it was not viable to sink expensive machinery into every gallery capable of yielding some good stone. Monks Park was therefore selected for mechanization because of its ease of access, its layout, and its potential in yield of excellent stone (see Plates 32 and 39). To substitute for the old picking and vertical sawing, a Samson coal-cutting machine was introduced. The coal cutter is a small track vehicle, well suited to move around on the uneven floor of the mines. It has a long mobile arm which can be set to any desired elevation and angle. Around the arm runs a chain saw with large cutting teeth. Set to cut horizontally, the saw moves in an arc at ceiling level and rapidly achieves the picking operation first from a left-hand and then a right-hand station at the rock face. The cutter is finally stationed centrally to remove the pointed projection left between the two arcs, and the picking operation is complete. Because of the radius of the mobile arm's arc the depth of cut is increased to eight feet, and also the width of the face is now increased from 10 feet under the ancient method to an average 15 feet. Another advantage in the picking operation is the 5-inch width of each cut made by the chain saw, so that the required cavity, 10 inches in depth, is made in two sweeps.

In the vertical cutting operation this width of cut represents a waste of good stone, but the speed of cutting more than outweighs the disadvantage. Vertical cuts are made to produce three blocks of stone each about 5 feet wide. These are freed at the base by using steel 'plugs and feathers' which use the principle of the old 'chips and wedges' more scientifically. First holes are bored with pneumatic drills: into each hole two inverted wedge shaped 'feathers' are fed, thick end in, and the plug—another wedge—is driven between the feathers, thin end in, to prise the block free. The blocks can now be hauled away with relative ease, for the wide cut of the chain saw provides ample space for chains to be positioned around them, and a pneumatic crane does the work.

Mechanization at Monks Park has increased the rate of production four-fold, but when stone from other mines is required the ancient method still applies (except at Westwood, where another Samson cutter is used). In the tradition of their ancestors the quarrymen have already christened the new equipment 'windy pick' and 'windy drill', and go happily about their unending task deep in the hills which, for want of epitaph, could simply claim 'from here came Bath'.

15

---⁂---

The Craft of the Mason

IN THE SEVENTEENTH CENTURY the Crown as an employer of the mason was waning in importance. The Banqueting Hall in Whitehall (the first major building in London made of Portland stone), had been erected at a cost of more than £15,600 between 1619 and 1622, itself a period of marked depression, but after this little building took place on behalf of the Crown for the rest of the century, with the notable exceptions of St. Paul's Cathedral and the Royal Hospital at Greenwich. Certainly the Tower of London, St. James's Palace, Hampton Court, and other buildings erected in previous centuries needed maintenance; but the nobility, gentry, and commercial classes were becoming more important as builders. The office of King's Master Mason survived into the 18th century. Benjamin Jackson was appointed in 1701 by William III, his appointment being successively confirmed by Queen Anne in 1702 and George I in 1715. On Jackson's death Nicholas Dubois was appointed, followed by William Kent in 1735 and finally Henry Flitcroft in 1748. But their tasks became increasingly insignificant.

The availability of bricks for small building operations tended to reduce the number of stone masons during the 17th century, though there was a considerable increase in their number in the last third of the century, particularly following the Fire of London. Recovery after the Restoration was checked by the Dutch war, the Plague, and the Great Fire, and there was panic in 1667 and again in 1671 when the Exchequer Stop brought ruin for many bankers. Business remained unsettled and depression lasted until 1674.

Estimated losses through the Great Fire of 1666 were 440 acres laid waste, 13,000 homes and 89 churches destroyed, 2000 people rendered homeless and overall losses estimated at a contemporary value of between ten and ten-and-three-quarter million pounds. The Fire may well have done something in burning down insanitary nurseries of the Great Plague. Statutes of 1666 and 1670 demanded that to avoid peril of fire in future and to secure gracefulness and uniformity in building, houses should be built of brick or stone or both, and should be arranged in streets and lanes marked out by the City of London authorities. Judges of the King's Bench were empowered to fix the price of bricks, tiles, lime, and the cost of their carriage; and the same Acts imposed the Coal Duty of 12d. per chaldron of coal brought into the City precincts.

During the 17th century the Worshipful Company of Masons was still discharging the trade functions it had inherited from the old mystery or craft guild, and in 1677 the company was granted its Charter by Charles II. This Charter was confiscated by James II, who for a consideration of £125 replaced it with one of his own dated the 9th February 1686; this varied the terms of the Charles II Charter and provided that the Court of the Company must all be members of the Church of England and be communicants. The company were happier with the Grant of Charles II and obtained an Exemplification of it under the Privy Seal of Queen Anne on the 1st June, 1702, in which the whole text of the Charles II Charter was recited. Among its other provisions the Charter stated:

'We would be gratiously pleased by our letters pattents under our great Seale of England to incorporate them [the masons] into a body politick to have perpetuall succession and to grant them such liberties, powers and privilages as to us in our Princely Wisdome shall seeme requisite and necessary for the better order rule and government of the said company and the members thereof and the improvement of the said art or mistery of masons by all jist and lawfull means and to the end they may be empowered to suppresse and reforme all abuses practised by persons who take upon them without sufficient skill and knowledge to work att the masons trade to the great damage of our Subiects.

155

'That all and singular masons Freemen of our said Citty of London and all other our subiects that now doe or hereafter shall vse the same trade art of mistery within our Citties of London or Westminster or the suberbs of the same Citties or seaven miles Compasse of the same on every side thereof by virtue of these presents shall be one body incorporate and politick in deed and in name by the name of Master Wardens Assistants and Cominalty of the art or mistery of masons of the City of London and we do really and fully make ordeine create erect constitute and declare one body Corporate and politick by the name aforesaid.

'And that by the same name they and their successors shall and may have perpetuall succession.

'The Master Wardens and Assistants for the time being or any five or more of them, of whom the Master and one Warden must always be two, should have full power and authority within the prescribed area of the City and its liberties were any stones to be used in the art or mistery of masonry shall be brought or laid, to search and see whether the same be of due goodness, measure length and thickness and whether the same be well and sufficiently wrought and if any such stones of what nature or quality so ever att any time vpon and after such view and search shall be duly and legally found to be ill wrought and not amended at the charges of the owner before the same be put to sayle or that any of them are so faulty that they cannot be amended and made good in Assize thickness and goodness that then the same shall be disposed of according to law.

'And for as much as wee are informed that many and great deceipts frauds and abuses are dayly used and practised chiefly by sundry persons who never duely served as apprentices to the said art or mistery of a mason and haveing noe Judgement or Skill therein wee therefore intending the speedy reformacon of the said abuses doe ordeine and firmly charge and comand that noe person or persons whatsoever from henceforth doe vse exercise or practice the art or mistery of a mason either as Master or journyman unlefse hee or they shall first have served as an apprentice or apprentices for the space of seaven yeares att the least unto a

156

freeman of the said company or to some other person lawfully vseing or exercising the art or mistery of a mason upon pain of being proceeded against according to the laws and statutes of this our Realme.

'Provided always and our Royal Will and pleasure is that nothing in these letters pattents centeined shall extend or be construed to extend to the preiudice obstrucon or hinderance of the erecting building and finishing of our Cathedrall Church of SAINT Paul within our Citty of London or any other church within the same Citty which were formerly burnt downe by the late dreadfull Fire which happened in London'.

The right granted by Charter to make searches was supplemented by an Act of Common Council of the 11th September 1694 under which ill-wrought and undersized stones were forfeited and broken by officials of the Mason's company. Thus after the general search of November 1701 which was ordered to be made throughout the trade 'for the correction of abuses now used therein', it is recorded in the Court Book that several Reigate stones were broken for being too thin. A few weeks later, and resulting from the same search, the Clerk of the Company was ordered to write to 'The Marblers of Swanage' and to Mr. Gilbert and Mr. Tobey at Portland with regard to the badness and undersize of the stone sent by them, and the Company's resolution to break the same whenever they found it. A general search was again held in 1704 as a result of which a small quantity of stone was broken and one or two workmen were reported for not being free. Despite this activity at the turn of the century, the trade functions of the Worshipful Company of Masons waned and may be regarded as of relatively little importance in the 18th century.

The old rule from the City of London regulations for the trade of masons dated 1356 that 'no one should set an apprentice to work except in the presence of his master' was clearly no longer enforced, if it still existed at all. By 1667, there were already several apprentices employed without their masters at Greenwich.

While in the Middle Ages those responsible for the erection or repair of cathedrals, abbeys, and castles commonly employed officials who kept accounts in considerable detail, the 'shop-keepers' and contractors of the 17th century usually employed no clerks for this purpose, and in most cases were 'unlikely to have put pen to paper themselves' to record details of their transactions. Hence the activities and use of journeymen in the 17th century have little record, although some information is provided in the bills paid to Artificers after the Great Fire, and in the bills of work done at Greenwich Hospital, records of which are preserved at Guildhall Library.

As early as 1620 there are records of an apprentice being bound to a freeman of the Company for a term of seven years. His master paid a fee of 2/6d. on signing his indentures, and at the end of seven years the apprentice was able on producing his indenture to take up the freedom of the Company and become entitled to work at his trade as a master and fellow of the crafts within the limits of the Company's powers. The fees on taking up the freedom were a gratuity of one pound, a fine of admission of three shillings and fourpence, and a clerk's fee of entry of sixpence, making a total of £1. 3s. 10d.

The freeman (as he now was) might subsequently take up the clothing and livery of the company, at which point he would pay a livery fine of £3, which might be increased to £6 if it was considered that he could afford it. This was termed a steward's fine, and freed him from being called upon to act as steward at the annual feast. If he progressed to join the Court of Assistants which was the governing body of the Company, a further fee of £2 was payable. Normally he would go on to become Renter Warden, Upper Warden and eventually Master of the Company, but if he declined the office of Renter Warden he paid a penalty of £10. With the notable exception of the scale of fees, these procedures are similar to those still followed by many of the City Livery Companies.

Within the framework of the Worshipful Company of Masons was an inner body described in the records as the 'Accepcon'. This was called the 'Inner Fraternity of Speculative Masons', and comprised the Masons Company Lodge, the members being known as accepted masons. The diarist John Aubrey writing on the reverse of an MS now in the Bodleian Library, made a note to the effect that a great convention of the fraternity of freemasons was to be held at St. Paul's Church in May, 1691. Having made the note Aubrey erased the word 'free' and wrote over it the word 'accepted', thus using the term for speculative or non-operative masons; it being his intention to allude to the society and not to the craftsmen.

The accepted masons of the 17th century were therefore the ancestors of the present Order of Freemasons who are no longer connected with the craft of masonry. The anomaly remained however that in 1717 the Grand Lodge of Ancient Free and Accepted Masons of England was born, for at that time many lodges were composed of operatives who were active masons, the non-operative members still being termed Accepted Masons. The word 'acception' may be otherwise rendered as 'The Lodge'. Extracts from the old records show that admission into the Company was not of esoteric character, whereas it was into the Lodge held under the Company's wing. Though they were in a sense independent (membership of the one not involving membership of the other), the minutes of both organisations are most valuable as illustrating the separation then existing between the mainly operative and the wholly speculative sections of the fraternity; they worked alongside each other as distinct societies.

The Masons' Hall Lodge of Speculative Masonry on March 10th 1682 admitted into the Fellowship of Freemasons Sir William Wilson Knight, Captain Rich. Borthwick, and four other members. Knight and Borthwick however were not members of the Worshipful Company of Freemasons, so that by this time it was possible for gentlemen masons to become members of the Lodge without the obligation of joining the Company or taking up the freedom of the City. This is as near to the point of separation of the Worshipful Company of Masons and the Order of Freemasonry as the records come.

This was a hundred years before the coming of the Industrial Revolution. The amount of stone quarried during the middle ages and up to the 16th century had been relatively small, but expansion during the 17th and 18th centuries in the freestone beds on Portland and in the Bath area 'changed the whole scale of the industry'. However one practice, known as early as the 14th century, had an interesting corollary. Progressively, architects for major buildings looked more and more for the best stone for the job, and had moved away from the old habit of using purely local materials. Hence it gradually became customary for masons to work near to quarries rather than at building sites. By 1851, there were already 30 masons living at Portland, working mainly on the Verne and the breakwater. In the next 50 years, Portland was to become the largest centre of masonry in the country, a fact which did not escape the notice of The Bath Stone Firms. In Bath itself, the number of masons resident in the City had increased from 41 in 1809 to 106 by 1829.

Portland stone was much used for the exterior of public buildings in London; it was not cheap, but its advantages were described by a contemporary in these terms: 'its hardness gives it many requisites for producing exquisite masonry. Most of our public buildings are composed entirely of this stone and it is frequently made use of in dwelling houses, for kerbs, strings, facias, columns, cornices, floors of halls, vestibules, and staircases. Portland is decidely the most handsome freestone known, being capable of bearing an arris in moulding equal to marble.' Fears that Bath stone might become a competitor because of the great expense of freight and duty on Portland stone were unfounded, for the Bath quarries and masons were fully occupied with their booming local housing programmes, and there was no cause for alarm.

Masonry in the Bath area was to continue as a fragmentary industry until the middle of the 20th century. At West Wells high in the hills east of Bath, the present masonry works was originally a cutting yard, or cutting works; here the company dressed stone which was then farmed out to sub-contracting masonry yards for carving to builder's specifications. These sub-contracting master masons included H. Head and A. Lambert at Corsham; K. Lambert, Chaffey and Norkitt, T and A Weeks, and Richards and Milson at Box Station; and Nowell & Carpenter, and A and H Cogswell at Box Wharf. The stone came down a horse tramway from Box Hill to Box Wharf for the purpose, and on the Wharf there was a wagon repair unit to cope with damage incurred in the perilous descent.

The Cogswell business ceased operations after the Second World War, but the other masons were brought into the West Wells yard in 1947 and 1948, so that West Wells became a masonry yard for finished stone. A central drawing office was opened at Bradford and was staffed by Cecil Lambert, Frank Richards, Herbert Head, and Frank Nowell, all drawn from the masonry yards. Up to the time the masons came into West Wells, all their work had been done by hand and they had been responsible for providing their own tools.

The modern system followed alike at Bottomcombe on Portland and at West Wells is for designs for the cutting and carving of stone to be prepared from architect's drawings; in many cases the particular stone to be used is selected by the architect, otherwise it is carefully selected by the manager of the mason's yard. A stone working drawing is prepared (alas, no more on linen) and when approved by the architect the individual stones on the drawing are numbered. For complex stones a setter-out then prepares zinc templates and production cards. Simple stones are generally made from dimensions marked on the production card. The production card travels with the stone as it is passed through the works.

The block stone from the quarry is first cut into a series of slabs of the required thickness, leaving the edges rough for cutting to the required lengths and widths at a later stage. The slabbing is done with a primary saw of 3 metres diameter, which has a blade sintered with industrial diamonds. The teeth on this saw are so arranged that it can cut stone approaching it from either direction, the stone being shifted across and brought back in parallel to cut the opposite face. The block then goes forward to the secondary or twin saw (also sintered), for cutting the remaining four sides; here two opposing faces are cut at the same time. The sawing process has become progressively sophisticated and now tables can be made to rise and fall allowing step cutting with checks and rebates; and gantry-mounted saws can be programmed to effect a series of cuts, speeding up production even more.

When large numbers of slabs of the same thickness are required, a frame saw is used. This consists of a horizontal frame containing between 10 and 25 diamond tipped steel blades, equally spaced and subject to very high tension. The frame, with its blades, is reciprocated horizontally by an electrically driven crank arm and is lowered automatically at a controlled speed, slicing the stone block into slabs of equal thickness at about 400 mm an hour. This method has the additional advantage of producing a high standard of finish on the cut surface of the stone, compared with the semicircular marks left by circular sawing, which have to be removed in subsequent processing.

For stone leaving the works as sawn slab, only primary and secondary sawing is required. Such masonry may be ready for paving, but will require dowel holes and fixing slots if used as ashlar—accurately dressed building blocks for laying in courses with thin joints. If the block has to be shaped with hand work to an architect's design however, the part of the remaining work which can be done by machinery is next identified, and planing machines with cutters are set in the reverse pattern of the template. The planing machine, working backwards and forwards, takes off an average of a sixteenth to an eighth of an inch of stone each time, to produce a finished profile; the block is then cut with a circular saw to the exact length required.

As an alternative to planers, grinding wheels are used to make checks, chamfers, rebates and similar profiles. These are usually mounted on machines universally adjustable for angle and direction of cut, and which can also be used by a change of tool for sawing. A battery of these machines can combine up to six operations in one pass, such as angle cutting, surface grinding, slot and groove cutting, and grinding rebates.

Finally comes the milling machine; this has a rotary action and works with a router on a spindle which is presented to the stone and can indent to almost any required shape. Another machine in the production line is the lathe, on which a block can be rotated when circular columns and similar rounded shapes are required.

When the machine work is done, a certain amount of finishing may yet be required and this must be done by hand. Where a milling machine is routing into a corner which has to be cut into a right angle, it inevitably must leave an unwanted rounded corner, and this has to be cut out by hand: this may apply, for instance, to the stoolings on a window sill. When geometrical work has been completed, for example on the capital of a corinthian pillar, the stone leaves the masonry works 'boasted', that is, with spare stone which the hand-working carver can cut away in reaching the final design. Today the vast majority of production goes out in various mechanically produced forms with a preponderance of simple ashlar; and only a small proportion, usually less than 10%, is worked by hand for specialized use, such as restoration of ancient buildings. Plates 40, 41, 42 and 43 illustrate the modern masonry processes.

16

The Stone Firms—1 Expansion

THE GROWTH OF the quarrying and masonry industries in the late 18th and early 19th centuries was dramatic, and may be attributed in some measure to the use of ashlar, or plain rectangular sawn stone blocks, for building private houses; the city of Bath is a supreme example of this development. Masons from different parts of the country converged on areas where building stone was quarried, to prepare cut stone for the building trade. It was a natural development that more masons were needed where steam power was already harnessed to step up the rate at which stone was quarried. At the time of the 1841 census there were 110 quarrymen in Wiltshire and over 1300 masons or stone cutters. Roads, canals and railways progressively made the transporting of stone cheaper and more feasible: hence a greater variety of stone was available, and it was no longer an advantage to use local stone or stone that could easily be shipped by sea or river to its eventual destination. The best stone for the job could at last be selected.

The market for Portland stone had always been wide because of access from quarries to water transport, whereas Bath had to wait for the Avon Navigation before shipment of stone via Bristol to other parts of the country became possible. The canal system extended the market for both, but worked more to the advantage of Bath stone which, from 1810, could be shipped direct to London via the Avon and Kennet Canal. In 1830, Betts and Drewe, Shaw & Company, and Clerke Robins & Company, all of

Bradford-on-Avon, were advertising conveyance by fly boat (lightly loaded horse-drawn vessels which moved continuously by day and night to a rough time-table), to London, Bath, and Bristol. Eleven years later the Box Tunnel was completed, thus opening up transport on the growing railway network. It was from this time that the quarrying industry in the areas to the east and south of Bath developed rapidly; in the next 20 years the number of quarrymen working in the hills increased to about 370.

By 1875 there were some 300 masonry yards of major and minor importance in the area surrounding Bath, and the quarrymen in the limestone beds were busy bringing to their notice stone in a subtle variety of specifications. Pictor & Sons of Box advertised Box Ground, Corsham Down, Farleigh Down, Combe Down and Bethel stones, with rates for delivery to all parts of the kingdom; dressings, both plain and ornamental, including vases, tombs, and chimney pieces were offered 'ready for fixing'. Randell Saunders & Co. Ltd., of Corsham, quoted similar prices of stone both at quarries and depots. In 1880, James Chislett, quarrymaster, stone mason, builder and contractor, of Stoke-sub-Hamdon, was advertising specifications and contracts for public buildings and private residences. 'Ham stone', he claimed, 'is very hard and durable, capable of a very fine finish, and wears a pleasing aspect. It is exceedingly valuable on account of its great resistance to fire and water.' And Jonathan C. Lano of Portland with H. Weller, his London agent at Nine Elms, were offering Portland block stone 'of the finest quality and any dimensions', and Portland roach stone 'suitable for engineering purposes'.

Despite the increase in volume of Bath stone quarried, the industry was in the hands of only a few companies: Job Pictor with a quarry at Box, Randell and Saunders with quarries at Combe Down, Corsham Down, Farleigh Down and Murchill Down, and Sumsions with quarries at Combe Down and Monks Park, had all been working since early in the 19th century. By 1880 the competition between these and other local quarrying concerns was intense. Between Corsham and Box, some 100 miles of mine had been worked out, and there was imminent danger of the separate operators overrunning each others' mining rights. Perhaps it was this restriction on development that caused a feud in the substantial Pictor family, in which a son of C. James Pictor moved away from the Corsham area with six quarry families to take over the unexpired stone rights in the quarries at Beer in Devon.

The competitive activities over and under the Wiltshire hills, coupled with the price-cutting war which accompanied them, led to the amalgamation of seven businesses in December, 1887. Joseph Pictor had been the father of three sons, Herbert Robert Newman, Cornelius James, and William Smith. It was Robert who planned the merger, but he died before operations started in the first week of 1888. The firms which came together in this way were: The Corsham Bath Stone Company Limited, R. J. Marsh and Company Limited, Samuel Rowe Noble, Pictor and Sons, Stone Brothers Limited, Isaac Sumsion, and Randell Saunders and Company Limited. Their main objects was 'to quarry and deal in stone, lime, cement, bricks, and terra-cotta'. The new company took the name of The Bath Stone Firms Limited. It was registered as a public company on the 27th of December, 1887, with a nominal capital of £250,000 in shares of £10 each. The original issue was subscribed by: R. E. Giles, Bath; G. Hancock, Corsham; S. R. Noble, Box; C. J. Pictor, Box; W. S. Pictor, Corsham; H. R. N. Pictor, Box; J. S. Randell, Corsham; A. W. Stone, Bath; J. Stone, Bath; Isaac Sumsion, Bath; and J. T. F. Turner, Bath. C. James Pictor became the Company's first Chairman and Managing Director.

The new Company took offices in the Abbey Yard at Bath and appointed Messrs. Tugnell Brymer & Co. as bankers 'provided our solicitor Mr. Inskipp be allowed to examine the Bank's balance sheet and that he report favourably thereon, and that this examination be repeated annually at the Bank's expense.' The Bath Stone Firms meant business. The first few months were spent in rationalizing the affairs of the vending companies and from the first day every effort was made to introduce economies, including a drastic reduction of the labour force. Instant working capital was put up by the vendors and repaid to them in April by a call of 12/6d. per share on shares allotted in the new Company. Everything pointed to a searing period of economy in which, for example, surplus railway wagons were sold to the Bute Wagon Works Company of Cardiff for a much needed £2500.

This internal spring clean did not deflect the Board from

resolving as early as January 10th, 1888 to undertake the sale of Portland and other building stones. The desire to enter the Portland stone trade was relentless, but not fanatic, and the policy of expansion was to be pursued for over 70 years in a manner combining ruthless purpose with oriental patience: everything would come to those who wait. Already in April 1888 Mr. B. C. White of Portland was offering to supply the whole produce of his quarries at 17/- per ton net, but wisely it was resolved only to place orders for stone as required. For the time being the new Company had to be content with merchanting arrangements, and conform with the tariff of the Portland merchant cards. This relationship soon led to reciprocal arrangements under which F. J. Barnes of Portland purchased and marketed Westwood Ground, Corngrit, and Stoke Ground stone at 9d. per foot cube loaded in rail trucks, and Box Ground, Farleigh Down, Corsham, Monks Park, Winsley and Combe Down at 10d. This was the beginning of a long association with the Barnes' interests although F. J. Barnes himself died intestate in 1913.

The Board never admitted that conditions in the building trade were good, but always saw reason why they might improve. Despite this caution, the Company averaged a profit of about £15,000 each year in its first 10 years, and in the years between 1898 and 1905 profits rose to an average of £32,000, despite very poor conditions in the building industry. This success gave the Company the power to expand, and this it achieved by three methods—by developing further reciprocal agreements for the merchanting of Bath stone and Portland stone, by purchasing Portland quarry and masonry companies, and by leasing and purchasing Portland quarry lands.

First, in 1898, came Mr. G. Shellabear of Plymouth, who had 'a preponderating influence' in the John Pearce Portland Stone Company Limited, to inform the Company of his willingness to sell the business. A little later Shellabear offered to sell his interest in John Pearce for £12,500. He held 600 founders shares, 1001 ordinary shares and £8000 of 6% first debentures. The directors investigated the Articles of Association of John Pearce and received Shellabear's assurance that he would be able to obtain leases of the quarries at Portland. Shellabear's solicitor confirmed 'the custom of Portland' as regards tenure of quarries so that the

Board might form its own opinion as to whether the leases held and promised were sufficient. The shares in Pearce were taken over by the Directors as trustees for the Company, and the Pearce Company were granted use of the Bath office staff to further its interests. The final amalgamation of the companies did not take place until 1948.

In 1889 the Company had agreed to purchase from W. H. P. Weston at Portland some three-and-a-half million tons of debris at 4d. per ton; this was to be supplied to the Admiralty for the new Portland breakwater, but the contract was apparently breached by the Admiralty and the Company went for damages against the Lords Commissioners. Whether for this or some other reason, the Weston undertaking was purchased by The Bath Stone Firms during that year, and with the purchase the Company gained the services and allegiance of H. J. Sansom who later became a director of The Bath Stone Firms, and of his son W. J. Sansom. The Sansoms were a boon to the Company, for there was little they did not know about Portland and the various operators who worked its precious stone.

The Sansoms knew R. D. Thornton, a director of the historic firm of Stewards and Company Limited, who had been the main suppliers of Portland stone 200 years earlier for the new St. Paul's Cathedral and the City of London churches, after the Great Fire. When Mr. Steward decided in 1900 to sell his business, negotiations for its purchase immediately started with The Bath Stone Firms. Mr. Steward wanted £83,000 for his business, cleared of all liabilities, but the Company were prepared to offer £35,650 for the freehold land and buildings at Portland, £700 for the barge *Harwich*, £5000 for the leasehold wharf at Grosvenor (which could be included or omitted as the parties might elect), and to take the plant, ridding, and stone at valuation, Mr. Thornton would be invited to take a seat on The Bath Stone Firms board. As a result Stewards agreed to recommend to their shareholders that the company was sold free of all liabilities for £76,000 'the profits from the 31st December 1899 to go to the purchasers, who are to pay interest however at the rate of 4% per annum on the purchase money from that date'. The secretary of The Bath Stone Firms was authorized to purchase Stewards business for a sum not exceeding £76,000 and at the 28th of March a memorandum was drawn up with an agreed figure of £73,000 for the business, subject to acceptance by the shareholders on each side; but Mr. Harold Brown, a shareholder in Stewards, raised an objection so that the price was finalized at £76,000.

Cooper Brothers in London were consulted on the issue of £100,000 debentures, largely for the purpose of financing the purchase of Stewards. The deal with Stewards was completed by the 25th of May, and the debenture stock was created at a board meeting on the 22nd of June; the Company's bankers now known as Messrs. Prescott, Dinsdale, Cane, Tugwell, & Company Limited, were made trustees for the debenture stock; and Mr. R. D. Thornton was appointed to take over the management of the Portland business and to be elected to the first casual vacancy on the board of The Bath Stone Firms. In June, Henry Sansom and W. J. Sansom were instructed to inspect several of Steward's quarries and land then being unridded by Mr. W. Hill, and to inspect other quarries at Combefield and new openings at Breston, where a new steam derrick crane had just been erected and was working satisfactorily. On the same visit the Sansoms and certain directors of The Bath Stone Firms examined the new buildings for stone sawing and working then being erected by the Pearce Company.

The Bath Stone Firms now had a big stake in Portland and might have rested for a while to digest the substantial increase in their interests; but the policy of expansion was to be on-going. In May 1904 the Company's solicitor, Mr. Titley expressed doubt as to whether the sub-letting of the Easton siding by Webber and Pangbourne Limited to Walter Webber and Walter Pangbourne as individuals and the onward assignment of the latter's rights to the Company would entitle The Bath Stone Firms to use the siding for loading 'stone other than that gotten or worked from the lands formerly belonging to Webber and Pangbourne Limited'. This dilemma may well have influenced the decision of the Company to purchase the assets of the Easton Stone Saw Mills at Portland belonging to Webber and Pangbourne Limited. The Easton Stone Saw Mills Company owned the important Bottomcombe Masonry Works and other stonework land and machinery. The company offered £3864 to Messrs. Webber and Pangbourne for the whole concern but Webber and Pangbourne through a Dor-

169

chester firm countered with a figure at £6620. Already the parties had agreed to the principle of an impartial valuation, and after consulting Messrs. Edward & Dawson, mining engineers of Cardiff, the business was purchased for £4750, by an issue of shares of the Company taken at market value. This was by no means the last investment made by the Company in Portland, but now the board turned its attention to expansion nearer home.

Since the middle 1890's, the board had been considering the acquisition of the Hartham quarries operated by Marsh Son & Gibbs Limited. Ten years later the much protracted negotiations for Marsh were still continuing and when a price was suggested by Mr. Philips on behalf of Marsh Son & Gibbs, the Company's secretary was instructed to say 'if the price asked were one half the sum mentioned it might provide a basis for negotiation.' A year later Mr. Philips put a price of £30,000 on his business, but this was again declined. When in 1909 The Bath Stone Firms asked for a stabilization of prices for Hartham stone between the Yockney Company Limited, The Hartham Park Company Limited and Marsh Son & Gibbs Limited, the directors of Marsh passed a resolution that 'the principle of a sale to or an amalgamation with The Bath Stone Firms Limited be adopted'. The writing was on the wall.

Within two months a receiver was appointed by the debenture holders in Marsh Son & Gibbs. The receiver was willing to treat with The Bath Stone Firms on the basis of selling all stocks of block stone at 6d. per foot cube 'except Stoke Ground', the plant at valuation, and worked stone at contract prices. The Company decided to take a short option on the understanding that nothing would be paid for goodwill or development, and that certain leases might be refused. In May 1910 all the documents were completed for the purchase of the Marsh undertaking, together with assignments of the various leases covering the land worked by Marsh. In their report to the shareholders, the directors described Marsh Son & Gibbs Limited as 'quarrymasters and merchants who had been a keen competitor of the Company'.

Early in the 20th century the Company took a yearly tenancy of the quarries at Combe Down from which Ralph Allen had won the stone to build regency Bath. In 1916 the proprietor, Captain Vaughan Jenkins offered to sell his business, the Combe Down

Freestone Company, but The Bath and Portland Stone Firms would not entertain the offer. Instead the terms of the yearly tenancy were revised: the annual surface rent of the Shaft Quarry remained at £2. 10s., but royalties were increased from 3s. 6d. to 4s. 6d. per yard, and the dead rent on the St. Winifred Quarry was increased from £55 to £75 per annum with royalties of £6 instead of £5. 10s. per perch. In March 1924 these arrangements were converted to a lease of 21 years. The normal lease of quarry land provided for an annual 'dead rent' which was payable whether the quarry was worked or not; in addition to the dead rent a royalty on stone taken out of the quarries was payable.

The Elm Park and Corsham Down Bath Stone Company Limited had been another competitor of the Company for many years, and in 1921 Mr. Alfred Taylor a director of the Company heard from William David on behalf of the Gastard Estate that the lease granted to the Elm Park Company was not to be renewed in 1933, when it was due to fall in. David had been General Manager of The Bath Stone Firms from 1897 for some years, having left David and Slant, quarrymen of the Forest of Dean, following abortive negotiations with the Company to take a 50% interest in his business. Mr. David might obtain for The Bath and Portland Stone Firms the reversion, with the option of additional land if the Company wanted it. By December 1921, the reversion and the lease of land not already let for quarrying was arranged for about £12,000. The Bath and Portland Stone Firms now played a clever hand, for when in 1926 W. A. Sheppard of the Elm Park Company applied to the Company for an extension of his lease beyond 1933, he was told that it was not possible to forecast the future, or to decide now what was to happen in seven-and-a-half years time: it was too early to come to any decision. However they indicated that it was not unlikely that The Bath and Portland Stone Firms might take over the quarries themselves in 1933.

In 1923 and again in 1926 the Elm Park Company encroached on the Company's quarry holdings: on the first occasion they broke through the Moor Park workings into the leasehold and freehold lands of The Bath and Portland Stone Firms at West Wells. A settlement was then arranged subject to an undertaking that in future the Elm Park Company would supply a certified copy of their surveyor's complete plan for yearly quarry workings, and an

171

undertaking that no further trespass would take place. However in 1926 there was an encroachment of the company's Spring Quarry holding and it was then decided to bring the matter to the notice of the agent of the landlord and a suitable fine was paid for the trespass.

Things were not going well for the Elm Park Company: unable to look foward, they could not inject new capital into the business. Shepherd approached the board with a proposal that Elm Park be transferred to the Company's benefit. The Company looked warily at £8200 worth of fixed and tangible assets plus the benefit of an export connection with America on the one hand, compared with £20,782 worth of debentures, mortgages, overdraft and creditors on the other, and the Company decided not to proceed with negotiations, 'even at the risk of the business going to the United Stone Firms (1926) Limited.'

By 1928 Messrs. Matcham of Bristol had been appointed receivers for the debenture holders, and Mr. Matcham made efforts to dispose of the Elm Park Company as a going concern. In March 1929 he asked if The Bath and Portland Stone Firms would extend their lease, but the board again replied that it was not possible to say now what the Company might be prepared to do in 1933 adding by way of disincentive that they did not even know with whom they would be dealing when that time arrived. But by November of 1929 a contract had been signed for the purchase of the property, stock, and plant of the Elm Park Company for the sum of £5050, immediate possession having already been given during early October.

In July 1920 The Ham Hill & Doulting Stone Company had offered to sell the whole of their interest in holdings at Portland to the Company. Their lands lay generally at the Grove and at the Headlands; it was decided to purchase these interests, though other holdings at Breston were regarded as unsuitable because of the depth of the ridding and doubts about quarrying after the ridded portion was worked out. These offers were accepted, and by May 1923 the possibility of the Company taking over the masonry works at Yeovil from The Ham Hill & Doulting Stone Company was also under discussion. A tentative offer of £5000 was made, but The Ham Company tended to regard the masonry works at Yeovil and their remaining interests at Portland as one indivisible concern.

Ten years elapsed and then the board learned that a receiver had been appointed by the Ham Hill debenture holders; and by May 1935 their works at Portland had been closed down. In the following Autumn an offer of £5500 was again made by the Company, this time to the receiver, for all the assets and effects of the Ham Company, and this offer was accepted, provided however that the receiver 'obtained a transfer of all leases to the new company that would need to be formed.' Frank Davis, one of the Company's masonry foremen at Corsham, became General Manager. The new company was registered as The Ham Hill & Doulting Masonry Company Limited, but by 1947 the company, which had served its purposes well, was virtually silent, and was later renamed The Ham Hill Doulting and Beer Masonry Company Limited.

The immutability of the Company's negotiating policies was exemplified well in their relations with the United Stone Firms Limited and their successors The South Western Stone Company. It took 50 years for this interest to come under the Company's control. In November 1909 the board expressed its readiness to enter into a friendly arrangement with the directors of the newly formed United Stone Firms at Portland. At that meeting they agreed to let 50 of the firm's railway wagons to the newcomers and a year later The Bath Stone Firms applied to the Commissioners of Woods and Forests for permission to load Portland stone belonging to United at the Company's Castleton Wharf. As the relationship grew, the Company offered old stock of Portland stone lying at Combefield and Nether Field to United at 20/- per ton on wagons ex quarry, subject to a minimum offtake of 50 tons per week; United were not to sell this stone at less than the Company's own prices and on similar terms.

But within three years United Stone Firms showed an unsatisfactory financial position and certain restraints were imposed on trading with them. By July 1913 a receiver had been appointed and it was agreed that should United wish to obtain stone from the Company they must pay cash in advance. It was arranged that supplies of Portland stone would be made on the orders of Mr. Harvey Preen, the receiver for United, upon his making himself personally responsible for payment. This was to be for the present only and to a limited extent on weekly terms. When United's Longsplatt (Box) quarry and the future of their Bath stone connection was discussed, the board deferred the matter and said it would be considered further 'when it was known who would have the power to bind United for the future'.

Under the careful management of Mr. Preen, the United Stone Firms survived, and early in 1927 the board noted that United had recently been reconstituted with H. J. Jack as chairman, and was to be known as United Stone Firms (1926) Limited. In the years that followed United Stone Firms tried to make private deals for Portland stone at prices under those agreed with the company, and at the end of 1928 United Stone were obliged to pass their dividend; at that time, according to Henry Sansom, only three cranes were at work in the United quarries at Portland. In December 1929 Jack met Taylor at United's Bristol offices, and there Jack stated emphatically that United would 'in future be conducted on an economic basis or otherwise it should come to an end.' In May of the following year, Jack suggested the feasibility of his company entering into some sort of an arrangement with The Bath and Portland Stone Firms for taking over United's production and sales. But when discussed by the board, Taylor was told that 'we should first endeavour to obtain payment of the balance owing by United Stone Firms', at that time £1140.

By the end of June 1930 United's balance sheet showed a loss of £28,500 for the previous 18 months, with provisions for a revaluation of stocks of £13,000, and loss on completion of contracts £7000, making a total loss for the period of £48,500 (to which had to be added a debit profit and loss balance of £3300 brought forward). There was also outstanding £8000 for preliminary expenses. United then applied to their shareholders for authority to issue a further £15,000 of debentures bringing their debenture total to £75,000. But their troubles were deeper, and by September 1931 United Stone Firms had been acquired by the South Western Stone Company of London. South Western had paid £44,000 for the United Stone business and The Bath and Portland Stone Firms agreed, when asked by Mr. F. Partridge of South Western, to continue with them the arrangements hitherto existing with United. South Western went on to enjoy a success in the Portland stone trade, and when much later, in 1960, South Western was at last taken over by the Company, The Bath and Portland Group became the largest producers of Portland stone.

The third way in which The Bath Stone Firms had set about

their policy of infiltration into the Portland stone industry was by the purchase or lease of quarrylands either from the government or companies who were not using them, or directly from the islanders who had inherited them under old manorial rights. When, in 1904 the Company purchased a one-half share of lawn 2387 at Breston from W. Pearce, the title still rested in a church gift and other documents which were all duly received. The Company had of course acquired lands through their purchases of Portland businesses, and when the full board of directors went to Portland in September 1910 they visited quarries already owned at Breston, Combefield, Weston, Suckthumb, Cowshades and parts of Wakeham and Inmosthay; the board were particularly concerned with consideration of accumulated dead rents on the Portland workings. In 1915 there was a sale of land belonging to the Lano family, and the Company purchased lots 41 (Bowlands) for £100; 47 and 48 (Netherfields) for £20; 53 (Combefield) for £270; 63 (Broadcroft) for £140; and 68 (Yeolands) for £950, a total of £1480. The same board meeting noted that Otter Brothers had purchased a lot at Wakeham with the intention of quarrying it themselves, and it was left to Henry Sansom to arrange the purchase of all their block stone; this was settled at 17/- per ton, the Company also 'providing crane pay rates and road dues and taking the risk of workmen's compensation'. In July 1915 another £800 was agreed to be spent on the purchase of lawns at Hodder's sale of land at Netherfield, Yeolands, Broadcroft and Combefield: at Combefield the company paid £2. 10s. for two twenty-fifths of lawn number 1932. The consequences of handing down quarry land 'undivided' on the Island of Portland is seen in an offer made to Mrs. Russell in October 1915 to purchase her late husband's interest of one twenty-first part each of lawns 2018 and 2013 for the sum of £20, 'the same amount as the Company paid for similar parts purchased from two other owners at Wattle Down, South-well'. The Company was constantly picking up fractions of lawns in similar fashion, and this contributed to a complicated pattern of company ownership which exists to this day. In April 1916 the Company became Crown lessees of Admiralty quarries for which they had tendered a dead rent of £200 per annum plus £5 a year for the surface and 4d. per foot cube for the stock of curf. A lease of other land from the Admiralty at Chene expired on June

30th 1920 and after much haggling this land together with the house upon it was purchased from the Admiralty for £3000. The annual report for 1925 noted that the Company had acquired from the executors of Mr. Woodman-Hill quarries and freehold land at Portland previously leased to the Company, while other freehold lands had been purchased 'for consolidating and strengthening the Company's holdings in Portland for many years to come'.

The Company was occasionally obliged to sell or lease land at Portland. In 1900 one-and-a-half acres of land on the West Cliff was sold to the War Department; in 1915 the Company affixed the seal to a deed between the Commissioners of Woods and the Company, surrendering two parcels of land adjoining Lloyds signal station at Portland, from the Crown lease of May 1911; and in 1921 a lease was granted to the Commissioners of His Majesty's Prisons for a piece of land at Yeolands for use as a recreation ground of the Portland Borstal Institution.

The buying of quarry lands was not restricted to Portland, and the Company continuously increased its holdings in the areas south and east of Bath. During 1905 the Company acquired a long lease of a large area of land 'in the Bath stone district' giving the Company control over more unquarried land than at any period of its existence. The dead rents were always a burden during periods of inactivity on leased land, and their concern is shown in an agreement made in 1913 with Lord Islington, owner of Hartham Park, to concede £170 a year on the Company's dead rent at Hartham Park from £770 to £600 a year; a similar reduction granted about the same time by Sir John Goldeney, brought the dead rent from £750 to £650 on the lease at Monks Park, though Sir John did agree to lease additional areas at the same time.

The Wiltshire quarrymen had never quite forgotten the stigma, arising from the Portlanders' allegation two hundred years earlier, that Bath stone was soft and hence not durable. These memories were stirred when in 1889 George Hancock, the Company's first manager, reported that he had inspected Portland stone in the Turbine House of the East London Waterworks, in the Lea Bridge Road, and also the new wing of the Deaf and Dumb Asylum at Margate where Westwood Ground stone had been dressed with 'the French indurating salts' in 1885. He found that the stonework at Margate was in perfect condition whereas the Portland cills at the East London Waterworks were 'fretting away'.

In May 1889 the Company's chairman, Isaac Sumsion Snr, with Hancock, was sent to Paris to investigate further the results of using the French hardening solution. This early extension in the field of stone seemed promising, and a year later an agreement was sealed with Faure, Kessler & Company of Clermont Ferrand in France for the sole agency in Great Britain and Ireland for the sale and use of the process known as Fluate for hardening and preserving stone. The Fluate solution was prepared by dissolving in ordinary water certain chemical crystals; the resultant emulsion when applied to the surface of the stone 'did not alter the colour or the granular appearance of it, and made it practically imperishable'. The cost of the solution, it was claimed, was trifling and the labour in applying it simple; in fact it was as cheap as whitewashing.

The directors felt that the invention was a valuable one and its adoption in this country would in many cases lead to the use of Bath stone 'instead of hard and expensive stones and other costly materials'. The directors were so pleased with Fluate that a book on the subject was rapidly prepared by their manager and sent out to shareholders, architects and builders. By December 1891 many architects 'including some of the most eminent members of the profession' were already employing the Fluate process upon numerous buildings, some being of national importance.

Three years later George Hancock consulted a patent agent in London to see what remedy if any the company had against the Northey Stone Company Limited, to whom the Company had sold Fluate on special terms, for manufacturing and selling their own compound as Fluate, which was clearly a matter of passing off. Under threat of legal action the Northey Stone Company gave an undertaking in October 1894 to discontinue advertising and selling Fluate, to render an account of their profits, to hand over all stationery bearing the word Fluate, to give the name of the manufacturer of their supply, and to hand over all stock. They further undertook not to use or cause to be used the word Fluate or any 'colourable imitation thereof'. The suppliers to Northey were

Davies and John of Old Bond Street, Bath, but no action was taken when they agreed to deliver up their stocks and not to infringe the Company's rights in future.

The Company tried vigorously to exploit its rights in Fluate, and Walter Pangbourne as London representative of the Company sold the compound in considerable quantities. But the last reference to Fluate in the Company's annals was for November 1914, confirming Walter Pangbourne's commission. By this time the Company could appreciate Bath stone and Portland stone for what they were: one was softer and easier for the mason to work; the other harder and over the very long term, perhaps more durable. By 1915 there was no longer a need to treat Bath stone with Fluate to simulate Portland stone, for it was all in the family: though occasional sales persisted for another 35 years. Fluate had served its purpose and had its day.

One late extension in the field of stone, a relatively small one, was not a financial success. In September 1927 the Company purchased from Fielding and Platt Limited, engineers of Gloucester, the business known as the Manu Marble Company, manufacturers by a special process of imitation marbles. Alan Pictor's brother Robert was put in to understudy the Manager, W. C. Dean, and five years later took over from him. Manu Marble made a notional profit once or twice but in almost every year up to World War II registered losses. Even as late as 1938 the board agreed to the purchase of new plant and machinery. But in 1943 the hydraulic presses at Gloucester were sold for £3725 to redeem some of the deficit. By this time Manu Marble, including its purchase price, had cost The Bath and Portland Stone Firms all of £30,000. Finally the stocks of block and Roman stones were sold in 1949 to Messrs. Walton Goody and Cripps at 26s. 6d. per yard. The board had better things to do with the Company's money.

17

---◆---

The Stone Firms—2 Money is Power: Power is Money

FROM THE BEGINNING, The Bath and Portland Stone Firms Limited was destined for success. The board by its earliest resolution, offered a range of Bath stone products at economic prices, and immediately went on to broaden that range by including merchanted Portland stone in its tariff. By dogged economy the Company prospered, and drew on its cumulative reserves to acquire first quarries and then masonry companies. Rising turnover produced increased profits, and increased control on standards and prices followed, with a gradual improvement of technology. The innate business instincts of the founder quarrymen is almost surprising: they were prudent, thrifty, long-sighted and patient; yet when the opportunity presented itself, they were not slow to appropriate capital for expansion. They sought good professional advice and acted upon it. In 1891, Cooper Brothers of London were appointed to audit the Company's books, and in 1895 Emberson and Hall, stockbrokers of Drapers Gardens in the City of London, were paid £100 upon their obtaining a quotation for the Company's shares on the London Stock Exchange.

The story of the Company is therefore one of progress based on good financial management. At the inception, £225,000 of its quarter-million authorised capital was issued, and from that time until 1921 the company was developed out of net profits, supplemented only by moderate bank borrowing and a debenture issue which was converted from time to time. Seventy-two years elapsed before the company needed to bring in a professional accountant as chairman; during 66 of those years the chairmen were drawn from three families: the Pictors and Sumsions, who had been founder members of the Company, and the Longs who were builders in Bath. In the remaining years the chairmen were Portlanders, one originally from Stewards and the other from Westons.

W. F. Long, speaking as chairman after World War II, told the shareholders 'since the Company's formation, trading results have shown a wide variation between hard and prosperous times. These fluctuations have been in large measure due to the fact that until the latter years, the Company's activities were confined to a section of the building industry which is extremely vulnerable to politics both national and international, and to general economic conditions.' There were, however, only six years in which 'hard times' produced a result of less than £10,000 net profit, and three of these, understandably, were during World War I.

With the dawn of the 20th century came a sense of disillusionment and hard reality. The 19th century had been a period of rapid empire building and scientific wonder; but the Queen was dead, and man's new found power was starting to turn against him as science was appropriated to the cause of death and destruction. The old order of life close to nature was dissolving, and Free Trade, under which England had flourished for half a century, was challenged by the new Imperial Preference. All this created a heavy air of uncertainty which affected industry throughout the country. The building trade, which shared this common experience, virtually controlled the progress of the Company from the beginning. The market for stone had been little more than average when the company was founded, and by 1900 sales of both Bath stone and Portland stone were falling away.

Without expansion, the good profits earned in the next six years could not have been achieved, for the building trade was experiencing a period of growing depression which culminated in 1906; the company had to make a liberal provision for bad debts and the dividend was contained only by virtue of the high value placed on accumulated stone stocks. Efforts to expand the market led to the development of some sales of Portland stone in Scotland, but

13th Century Lacock Abbey: the Cloisters.

Longleat House, near Warminster, was built in Bath stone during the
15th Century.

(Above) Stone wharf at Corsham Station, circa 1905.
(Below) Stacking ground at Spring Quarry, Corsham.

(Above) Scappling stone blocks by hand and saw.
(Below) Spring Quarry, Corsham. Ten thousand tons of Bath stone,
mostly destined for sale as ashlar.

(a)

(b)

(c)

(d)

In the mines at Hartham Park, Corsham: (a) hand sawing (b) cutting out bottom beds (c) cutting a breach cut (d) hand picking (a simulated photograph).

(Above) Hand sawing at Monks Park. The saws were seven feet in length and ten inches in depth.
(Below) By the modern method, the bottom is cut out with an Arc Shearer.

(Above) A modern crane, designed by John Lister-Kaye, in use at Monks Park.
(Below) Now the stone is winched up from the Monks Park mine by electric motor.

(Above) One of the original steam tractors, purchased from Lano at
Portland in 1913, draws two trailer-loads of stone.
(Below) A general view of Bottomcombe masonry works after the
extensions and conversion to electricity in 1931.

speculative building was everywhere at a standstill, and sales were continually affected by *force majeure* in one form or another. The Company's growing interests in Portland had been the Company's salvation, and in November 1911 the Company's name was changed to The Bath and Portland Stone Firms Limited.

There were problems to face other than conditions in the building trade, however. Exceptional wet and stormy weather from time to time had a grave effect not only upon the area of the Company's operations—particularly Portland—but also upon the movement of the company's product. In November and December of 1910, storms restricted demand in the home market and prevented the execution of orders for several cargoes of Portland stone which should have been shipped during 1910 but were delayed into the following year. And when the directors reported on the company's performance in the first half of 1912 when a notional £55 net profit was registered, the shareholders were told 'the past half year has been quite abnormal: the great colliers' strike, followed by dock troubles affecting one of the Company's most important fields of operation, paralysed for a time all building, and greatly aggravated the depression under which the building trade has suffered for some time past.' By the end of that year profits had picked up somewhat, but despite hopes for an improvement in the building trade the profit level was not to be restored before World War I.

The Company invited Charles H. Long of the Bath building contractors, J. Long and Sons, to join its board of directors in 1912. But if this gave The Bath and Portland Stone Firms an insight into the problems of the building trade, it certainly failed to provide any answers. Building continued in recession and a lock-out occurred in the London building trade during the first half of 1914. On this situation the directors commented 'notwithstanding the lock-out in the building trade the profits are sufficient to justify a 5% interim dividend. In coming to this conclusion, the directors have not lost sight of the fact that the building trade is likely to be seriously interfered with for a time, owing to the European War and the consequent financial disturbance; but they feel there is need for money to be circulated as freely as possible and that the shareholders will approve their action in not withholding the payment of a dividend at the present juncture.' Profits were sustained in 1915, but by the end of that year pre-war contracts were drawing to a close, and there was no inducement for owners to embark on fresh building enterprises.

Now the storage of munitions in the Company's mines at Corsham led to some amelioration of the Company's position. In 1915, by an agreement with the Director General of Explosives, the Company were appointed contractors for adapting and equipping mines at Corsham for the storage of munitions, and for storage maintenance. Under the Defence of the Realm Act, the whole of the Monks Park and Ridge mines were taken over, and a basis agreed for submitting claims to the War Department. In January 1916 the Company directors met General Savile and Colonel Kempster who inspected the mines with the Company's manager, T. Sturge Cotterell. The officers expressed their extreme satisfaction with the equipment at the mines and the way the munitions had been handled and stored. They requested that Sturge Cotterell should be authorised under a minute of the board to act as Superintendent of the mines and carry out all the Company's contractual obligations.

The officers said it would be a great advantage if Sturge Cotterell's services could be made available for the purpose of advising in the establishment of magazines in other parts of the country, and finally asked for the board's consent to release their general manager to undertake these duties for the Ministry of Munitions, and to this the board agreed. Sturge Cotterell accordingly became Superintendent of Munitions Stores under the Ministry of Munitions, and tendered his resignation as General Manager of the Company. The Royal Commission on Defence of the Realm Losses provided compensation of £1175 per annum for Monks Park and £100 per annum for the Ridge quarry.

Although the management of the munitions stores was thus out of the hands of the Company, the board noted that an accident occurred at Monks Park while in the occupation of the government; an iron coupling-hook broke, causing a trolley loaded with munitions to fall from ground level to the foot of the shaft. Fortunately, it was stated, there was no injury to persons, but two trolleys were damaged and there was 'some wastage of munition materials.' The snapping of the hook was attributed to a flaw in the iron, and was 'a pure accident.'

The directors had given up hope that there might be improvement in the building trade before the war ended. 'That trade', the directors

182

told the shareholders, 'is regarded by the government as one of the country's non-essential industries, and in these circumstances after two and half years of war the situation might very well be worse.' It did in fact get worse, and the level of losses in 1916 and again in 1917 exceeded £6000. The morale of the board of directors was now so low that when Alfred Taylor reported on two interviews with Walter W. Jenkins of Torquay and a Mr. Martyn of Cheltenham respecting 'a proposal made by them on behalf of a financier to purchase the whole of the Company's share capital,' the board expressed itself in favour of recommending the scheme to the shareholders for their adoption, in the event of its being proceeded with, within three months on 'the basis indicated.' There is no record in the annals of the Company of this basis nor any further reference to the negotiations. The impulse to give away the benefits of thirty years work was evidently frustrated, and the danger abated.

When the war was over, the Directorate of Lands of the War Office reinstated the Monks Park and Ridge mines, and the War Office decided to burn what was left of the TNT remaining in store in the Monks Park mine; it was proposed that this should be done 'on top of the rubble heap outside.' The board felt it wise for Alfred Taylor to consult with Lady Goldeney, the occupier of Monks Park, before any definite steps were taken 'so to destroy the explosive.'

After the war, costs were increasing rapidly, and the quarrymen and 'other workers in and around the quarries' at Portland were joining the Operative Stone Mason's Society in large numbers. The board reacted by increasing the selling price of block stone by 6d. per foot cube to cover higher wages and the rising costs of transport by rail. The wages agreement arrived at with the Portland quarrymen granted an increase over the pre-war level of 50% for handling rubble, and $33\frac{1}{3}$% for handling cap stone and quarry stone. At the same time there were troubles in the building trade which it was feared would again affect stone prices. A national settlement of building wages and conditions was to be negotiated to produce a state of greater stability in the trade. However in the early twenties many important building schemes were being contracted, and despite unrest among the builders the Company profits were once more on the increase.

The Company needed money to finance its work in progress and the 4% debenture stock due for redemption in June 1920 was reissued at 7% from the 1st January of that year, for repayment in 1925. In the following year the remainder of the unissued ordinary shares of the Company were allotted bringing the issued capital to £250,000. Abnormally good conditions during the three years 1925–1927 raised the Company's annual profits above £50,000, but as competition stiffened the profits dropped back to £37,000 in 1928. This was the year of a new Companies Act, and the board decided to revise the Company's articles of association which had been drawn up 40 years earlier. They also split the Company's £10 shares into units of £1 each. (Three years later the Company converted its shares to ordinary stock, thereby removing the clerical work of transferring shares with distinctive numbers.) In 1929 profits remained at an average level of £40,000, and the board decided to write off quarry leasehold lands and buildings, tramways, and goodwill to the value of £17,500.

Contracts for many exceptionally large and important buildings in London and the provinces, were awarded during 1930 and resulted in a record profit of £71,000, and a continuing demand kept the Company's quarries and masonry works operating at high pressure. When in 1931 a similar profit was recorded, the board with typical reservation attributed the Company's success to the large contracts secured in the previous year 'before the national economy campaign set in', a somewhat oblique reference to the financial crash of 1931. The directors referred to 'the general industrial depression and monetary stringency which were holding up further building to a considerable extent, and would necessarily lessen the demand for the Company's products until the financial position changed.'

In the next year, the Company's quarries were reduced to part-time working and profits at £37,000 were almost halved. As the depression intensified the profits dropped to £10,000 in 1933 and though in 1934 profits were better at £25,000, the directors feared that a return to the prosperous conditions ruling before the crisis of 1931 could not be anticipated for some time. By December of 1935 however stagnation in the building trade was passing, though the outlook was not yet promising enough to justify a return to full time working at Portland.

The profits edged up slightly in the following three years and in 1938, when the Company was 50 years old, the shareholders were reminded that dividends paid since the Company's inception had averaged approximately 10½%. With this comfort, given to the shareholders during the spring of 1939, the directors went on to anticipate the future with confidence—perhaps with more confidence than was justified: 'in view of the disturbed national conditions prevailing for the greater part of the period under review, which have undoubtedly had the effect of shelving and postponing building schemes, your directors feel that the trading result is satisfactory, and that with more tranquil conditions they can look forward to the future with confidence.' 1939 was not the best time to talk of tranquil conditions; six months later came the war and building was brought almost to a standstill. The Company was forced to eliminate from the balance sheet substantial stock values which were regarded as 'unmarketable in these abnormal circumstances'.

In the Company's first 50 years, net profits had totalled £1,547,000 which in real terms would have been worth many times that sum today (see Fig. 7 page 228). With those apparently small returns The Bath and Portland Stone Firms Limited had made itself pre-eminent in the field of building stone; it had survived the force of national and international politics; it had fought many hard battles with nature; and it had served the building trade faithfully, often in trying times. It had demonstrated by its careful husbandry of finance that money was the passport to power.

The board of directors were first and foremost quarrymen, and because of their knowledge of the hard conditions of early quarrying they were alert to the benefits that the Industrial Revolution could bring. They were slow in putting them into effect however and followed Alexander Pope's caution: 'be not the first by whom the new is tried, nor yet the last to lay the old aside.' As the Company acquired property in Portland, stone was still being won there by 'reaming'—the splitting of rock by a line of quarrymen hammering wedges in unison along a line of shell where it would laminate; horses were still dragged downhill on their haunches as brakes, behind enormous stone blocks, and in harness they still hauled stone over a network of railway lines laid down throughout the island. Hand derrick cranes were still used with chain falls (until wire ropes from a shipwreck took over from the chains), and it was a common occurrence for these derricks to topple over before the stone they were supposed to lift was clear of the ground.

Progressively power driven vehicles and tools were brought in to make each task easier. The Blondin overhead rope system of suspended tipping buckets (named for Charles Blondin, the French tight-rope walker) was introduced to speed up and save labour in the removal of spalls and ridding. In 1900 Anderson & Son offered to supply an electrical plant with generating engine complete, a picking machine with three heads, and a channelling machine wired to electric motors, all for the sum of £1500. This offer was not accepted, but it is interesting because there was insufficient water on the Island of Portland for the generation of hydro electricity; main electricity was not fed to the Island from the mainland until some 32 years later. However an offer by Anderson to supply a second-hand channelling machine for £250 was accepted (with an option to return it after a month if it failed to work properly).

In 1902 the Portland railway which had stopped at the northern end of the Island was extended by a circuitous route near the east coast and was brought into Easton. It was intended for the export of stone from the Island by rail, but this proposed method was never adopted, as it was cheaper and more convenient to export stone by water. A further scheme, a Company one, was the development of a pier at Church Ope to save the cost of transport either by the Easton and Church Hope Line or down the Merchant Railway to Castletown, but this plan also failed to mature. Later on the Company purchased the disused railway line between Easton and Castletown, and the Navy took over the Castletown end. Horses started to give way to steam in 1913, when the Company purchased three traction engines together with a number of wagons from Lano at Portland for about £1000. But the Company at Portland carried on with the use of hand derrick cranes for lifting stone and steam tractors for shifting it until well after the First World War. In May 1917 it was decided to close the Merchants' Railway at Portland, but two years later it was re-opened and continued in use until 1939.

The Bottomcombe masonry works at Portland were brought up to date with the installation of new equipment and machinery in 1923. A new oil engine and generator were put in, with additional cutting machines and saw frames, and a new steel gantry was erected with three electric travelling cranes. The question of supplementary power was discussed and the Company's engineer Ballantyne prepared a scheme for a central power station to serve No. 1 and No. 2 yards. It was decided to extend the existing setting-out shop in No. 2 yard by doubling its length, and Ballantyne was again called on to plan the re-building of the masons shed in No. 2 yard and a new smithy (which necessitated the removal of the John Pearce Portland Stone Company's offices into a 'suitable army hut'). The Company purchased its first steam crane from the Admiralty in 1924; thereafter the cranes were converted to steam from time to time and in the mid 1930's were again converted from steam to electricity.

The board heard of a pneumatic tool that had been seen working in London on Portland stone, and in 1925 a committee was formed to inspect this tool with a view to its use at the Portland Masonry Works. In the following October the board discussed a pneumatic picking machine installed by the Elm Park and Corsham Down Bath Stone Company Limited at Elm Park quarries. It was thought that while quicker in action, it might prove more expensive than the hand picking previously employed in the Company's mines, and no further action was taken. However in 1926 the question of pneumatic machinery was considered in relation to its general use at Portland and by February 1926 pneumatic tools were adopted there. Self-generated electricity was used at Portland from the late 1920's up to the early 1950's, when the mains supply came in. In 1932 the Company ordered four Sentinel steam wagons at £1,145 each and immediately the old steam tractors were sold at giveaway prices: for instance, £80 was the asking price for two of the old tractors (see Plate 40).

During all this time the ancient method had been used for mining stone in the Bath area and only in December 1937 did the Managing Director consider the possibility of mechanizing the mining operations to some extent. By October of 1938 a quarrying machine had been built on the lines of a coal cutter and it was not until January 1948 that an arc shearer was purchased and delivered for use at Monks Park to replace the old picking method.

The Company had always enjoyed good relations with its

workers, first with the quarrymen and later on with the masons as this side of the business developed. At first sight, the numbers who took part in the annual outing to Bournemouth in August 1893 may suggest an exaggerated appreciation of the quarrymen: enjoying the day were 'our own men, 222: boys and youths in our employ, 102; our men's wives and children, 119; and visitors, 110: a total of 553. But the net cost of this outing was a mere £6 4s. 1d. In the light of this expense, life in those days was not valued quite so cheaply as it may seem at first. When in May 1888 a block of stone fell on William Mumford, killing him at No. 6 Quarry, Corsham, his widow was awarded £5, to be paid at the rate of 3s. per week. Fortunately there were few such accidents, but in January 1900 Frederick Wooton, one of the sinkers, fell out of the lifting box down No. 3 Shaft at Corsham, after being partially overcome by fumes of powder during blasting. It was therefore resolved in September of 1900 to insure the Company's workmen against accidents in the Bath district with the Commercial Union Insurance Company; the rate was 7s. 6d. per quarryman, 5s. for masons and 2s. per £100 wages of the staff.

The working of short time occurred at Portland in 1906, in 1923, and again in 1924—caused always by strikes or lock-outs in the building trade; but this did not affect the Company's relations with its many employees. When in 1930 the secretary of the Amalgamated Union of Building Trade Workers at Portland wrote to Alfred Taylor confirming the acceptance of an offer made by the Company, he wrote: 'the employers agreed to stabilise the present wages for three years against a reduction, but should the cost of living figures warrant an increase in wages according to the terms of our agreement, this increase in wages to take effect. Will you please forward a signed agreement to this effect.' Alfred Taylor replied 'the employers hereby adopt a resolution as set out in your letter to remain in force until the 30th of June 1933 subject otherwise to the general terms of the existing rules and schedules. I hope that the same good relations between your members and the employers will continue to exist for many years to come.' The hope was certainly fulfilled.

Through all the years, The Bath and Portland Stone Firms were not merely 'hewers of stone'. As stone came to be cut and carved in mason's yards near the quarries in the mid-19th century, the mason's responsibilities increased greatly, and now they worked with architects and builders to very finely drawn specifications. But from the very beginning the company was also selling block stone into builders' stocks, and supplying roadmaking and other stone of inferior quality in vast quantities. It is only possible here to indicate by a few examples the broad spectrum of the Company's activities in its first 50 years.

In October 1895 a cargo of 1000 cubic feet of Bath block stone for Samuel & Son of Montreal was delivered free on board a vessel at Bristol at 8d. per cubic foot. By 1914 stone dust was being sold to the Highways Construction Company for roadmaking. In December of that year Portland stone was being supplied for building the County Hall, Westminster: the contractors were Holland and Hannen Limited. In the following year Bath stone quarry spalls (weathered stone fragments) were required for road foundations for Army camps on Salisbury Plain. In February 1916 60,000 cubic feet of Box Ground stone was supplied for the exterior of Bristol University and Westwood Ground stone was supplied for the interior: the builders were Wilcox & Co.; for this contract, the price of stone started at 1/6d. per cubic foot and advanced to 1/10d. in 1919 and 2/1½d. by 1921.

An 'important committee' was appointed in November 1920 under the chairmanship of Sir Aston Webb to determine the most suitable stone for the restoration of Westminster Abbey. The committee unanimously recommended Whitbed Portland stone from the Wakeham quarries. In March 1927 the new headquarters of I.C.I. were being built on Millbank to the design of Sir Frank Baines. Sir Frank sent Dr. Alan Howe of the Geological Museum and Government Survey Office to select the stone required from Portland; the report was extremely favourable, and the contract went finally to United Stone Firms. In March 1934 stone from the Broadcroft quarries at Portland was supplied for the building of a new gallery that Sir Joseph Duveen was presenting to the Tate; the interior was constructed with some 16,000 ft cube of Corngrit and Copenacre stones, the exposed surfaces being treated with Fluate. Sir Joseph Duveen had also promised the British Museum a new gallery to house the Elgin Marbles, and 17,000 cubic feet of Portland stone was supplied in place of the French marble originally specified. In February 1936 a massive quantity of debris was supplied for the Portland Breakwater.

As the Company progressively turned to steam power, pneumatic tools, and electricity during the 15 years after World War I, so its capacity to quarry and dress stone soared. In its peak year, 1929–30 the volume and weight of stone sold was truly remarkable. Power had been the key to increased turnover and greater profits. The popularity of Portland stone may be gauged by listing some of the contracts running in London alone during that year (there were many more in the provinces).

The *Daily Telegraph* building, in Fleet Street, was built in Portland stone: the architects were Elcock & Sutcliffe and Sir John Burnet & Partners, and the contractors were James Carmichael (Contractors) Limited; Lloyds Bank headquarters, where the elevations to Lombard Street and Cornhill are all in Portland stone: the architects, Sir John Burnett and Partners and Messrs. Campbell Jones and Smithers, and the contractors, Trollope and Colls Limited; Port Soken House, in Aldgate: the architects, G. Val Myer, and the contractors John Greenwood Limited; the Royal Mail Steam Packet Company's head office, with elevations to Leadenhall Street and Lime Street in Portland stone: architect, Sir Edwin Cooper, and contractors, Trollope & Colls Limited; Broadcasting House in Portland Place (see Plate 44): architects, G. Val Myer and Watson-Hart, and contractors, Holland Hannen & Cubitts Limited; Chiltern Court, Baker Street: architect, Charles W. Clark, and contractors, Higgs & Hill Limited; the Holker Law Library, Gray's Inn, where Portland stone carvings are included: architect, Sir Edwin Cooper, and contractors, Trollope & Colls Limited; Moorgate Court, the headquarters of the Ocean, Accident & Guarantee Corporation Limited: architect Sir Aston Webb, and contractors, Dove Brothers Limited; the Commercial Union's head office in Cornhill, where Portland stone is used with generous relief in sculptures by Walter and Donald Gilbert: architect, Sir Aston Webb & Sons; Friday House at the west end of Cheapside, built in red brick with Portland stone dressings and sculptures: architect, R. G. Muir and contractors, Acme Construction; Thames House, in the same style as the I.C.I. headquarters (also built, a year earlier, in Portland stone), and linked with it by a bridge over Page Street, each half erected at a cost of approximately £2 million: architect, Sir Frank Baines, and contractors, John Mowlem & Co. Limited; Cunard House, Leadenhall Street (see Plate 44), with a frontage in Portland stone: architect, Mews & Davies; High Holborn House, with all frontages built in Portland stone: architect, George Vernon, and contractors Messrs. Fairhead Allen and Sons Limited; National House, Moorgate: architects, Messrs. Henry Tanner & Son, and contractors, Trollope & Colls Limited; Punch Offices, Bouverie Street, built in red brick with Portland stone dressings and scultpures: architects, Thompson and Walford, and contractors Messrs. Dove Brothers Limited.

The list of superb buildings in which Bath stone and Portland stone has been, is being, and will be used is never ending; but during the period since World War II new skills, methods, and techniques in the use of stone have been introduced. One result of this is the balancing of increased cost of stone against the much reduced quantity now required to produced the same visual effect. This is part of a remarkable story that will be told of diversification which the Company has achieved in one third of a century since the war.

18

---·⚜·---

Portland and the War Graves

WHEN IN 1859 Henri Dunant, a Swiss banker and philan-
thropist, set out from Geneva to meet Napoleon III in Italy, he
chanced upon the battlefield of Solferino where he was shocked to
find some 40,000 dead and injured, abandoned and helpless. With
a few volunteers Dunant set to work to tend the dying and rescue
the living. As a result of his subsequent campaigning the International Red Cross was formed in Geneva some four years later,
and under the terms of the First and Second Geneva Conventions
the Red Cross has been a neutral intermediary in warfare from
that day forward. In a situation that had certain parallels Fabian
Ware, who was sent to France in charge of a British Red Cross
Unit in 1914, was likewise shocked at the disorder and indignity
of death on the battlefields around him. The dead had fought for
something more noble than to lie twisted, cold, and forgotten,
often lacking the decency of the rudest burial. Already the British
and Germans, through Geneva, had a convention for telling if a
missing man had been taken prisoner, and information about the
dead was obviously relevant. But Ware and the members of his
'Red Cross Mobile Unit', as it came to be called, became
increasingly interested in the graves themselves and in their
maintenance.

Ware's enthusiasm for this work may be measured by the fact
that within a matter of weeks of the commencement of the war he
concluded an arrangement with Lord Robert Cecil, chief of the
British Red Cross in Paris, to exchange information about missing
British soldiers, and it was at Bethune cemetery in October 1914

192

that Ware met Dr. Stewart, a Red Cross medical assessor. Here they found English graves carefully marked with plain wooden crosses, but Ware realized that there was no register of their position nor was anyone responsible for their maintenance. The crosses had been made by comrades of the dead from Army soap boxes, and bore inscriptions that were rapidly becoming illegible.

Many graves lacked even such rudimentary inscriptions, and there were other instances where bodies were mutilated beyond recognition or blown to pieces, or buried without any identification at all. Often a grave supposed to contain the remains of one soldier turned out to be a pit into which large numbers of dead had been thrown by the enemy; in many such cases the bodies still bore their discs which helped with identification. Ware and his unit carried out their work with reverence and where such bodies were discovered they were laid out side by side and the burial service read over them. Ware soon forced his way into the presence of General Macready, Adjutant-General to the British Expeditionary Force, to plead his cause for registering and marking British graves. Macready was impressed and by March 1915 Ware was able to report to the Red Cross in London that his Mobile Unit had been officially recognized as the only organization authorized to deal with the question of the locality, marking, and registration of the graves of British officers and men in France; and that he was to operate under the title of 'The Graves Registration Commission'.

By that time Ware's work was officially recognized by General Haig himself who conceded that 'though this work does not directly contribute to the successful termination of the war it has extraordinary moral value to the troops in the field as well as to relatives and friends of the dead at home. In May 1915 Ware reached agreement with the Red Cross that his unit's work was separate; he gave up his ambulances, but the Red Cross continued to provide vehicles and personnel to help in his work. By October Ware had built up his own organization covering the Western front and had prepared records which classified burial grounds, the number of graves in each, and details of individual graves: already over 30,000 registrations of graves had been made.

In September 1915 Macready recommended to the War Office that the Graves Registration Commission be placed on a proper footing as a part of His Majesty's Forces, thus ending its dependence on the British Red Cross. This transfer enabled Ware to move with much greater freedom along the whole of the Western front, and Ware soon concluded arrangements with the French government to provide burial grounds for the British and Allied troops, and to allow the British to appoint 'an association which could take over responsibility for maintenance'.

Now the statesmanlike qualities which Ware was able to contribute to the development of the Commission started to reveal themselves. Basically Ware felt that all ranks became comrades in arms when living together in appalling circumstances, and he began his long campaign against the distinction and treatment of dead soldiers and their graves by rank. He knew for instance that officers themselves in 99 cases out of a 100 would wish to be buried among their men and not to have their graves preferred in any way. Ware stopped exhumations and in 1915 obtained an order from the Adjutant-General forbidding them; in the following year permanent memorials 'which could do so much to mark social differences between men' were banned by the army. Thus Ware started to build up a spirit of democratic equality which not only had to be understood by relatives of the dead but also had to conform with the tenets of many different religions.

The next step was the formation of a national committee for the care of soldiers' graves. The committee would take over from the army at the end of the war, and under the presidency of the Prince of Wales, included Ware and General Macready, with two representatives of the French military authorities. Early in 1916 the Graves Registration Commission was re-titled The Directorate of Graves Registration and Enquiries; by May of that year the Directorate had registered over 50,000 graves and answered 5,000 enquiries. Ware moved to an office in London and 'acquired the frivolous title of Lord Wargraves'; in August he was promoted to the rank of Brigadier-General.

At every turn Ware's work was increasing in breadth; by the end of 1917 negotiations had been completed with Belgium, Egypt and Greece for the grant of lands for war graves. A programme of horticultural work to keep the cemeteries in suitable condition had been instituted under the care of Arthur

Hill, the Assistant Director at Kew Gardens, working with A. C. Blunt, the member of Ware's staff who had first had the idea of extending the gardening work in France into a full system of horticultural treatment. With the heavy losses sustained in the Battle of the Somme came new problems. The recovery of the dead from no-man's-land apparently ranked low in the risks worth taking, and often soldiers were forced to live with their dead. Just before their famous attack on Vimy Ridge in 1917 the men of the Canadian Corps 'of their own initiative and with the assistance of the Directorate marked out land, dug trenches, and made all arrangements for the burial of the killed in the forthcoming action'; within 24 hours of the attack all the graves were marked and recorded. By April of 1917, 150,000 graves had been registered in France and Belgium with a further 2500 in Salonia and over 4000 in Egypt. Seventy cemeteries had been planted.

Ware now thought ahead to the end of the war when the organization taking over from the army would face the task of commemorating the half million soldiers who had fallen as well as the records of the graves in which they were buried. Ware felt strongly that this new body must be imperial and not national since many soldiers from the Dominions and colonies were among the dead. To this end Dominion representatives were invited to sit on the Prince of Wales Committee and on April 13th, 1917 the Imperial governments approved proposals whereby King George V would constitute by Royal Charter the Imperial War Graves Commission. The Prince of Wales became its President: the Secretary of State for War its Chairman. Fabian Ware was appointed Vice-Chairman of the Commissioners so that he could co-ordinate the work of the Army Graves Service which had to prepare the graves and the new commission which had to look after them.

The Commission had no precedent for the standards it was about to set but the various problems and principles involved duly found their solutions. Among its major decisions were the location, design, and number of cemeteries; and the parameters governing the headstone of the individual dead soldier. For the general principles involved, the Commission looked to the Director of the National Gallery, Charles Aitken, and two of the countries' most distinguished architects, Edwin Lutyens and

Herbert Baker. The three went to France but came back with confirmed differences of opinion. Ware then consulted Sir Frederick Kenyon, Director of the British Museum, who had served in France with the Inns of Court Regiment.

Kenyon was an inspired choice; he came back from France with firm and sensible recommendations. Cemeteries were to be marked by rows of headstones of a uniform height and width, the graves themselves being levelled to a flat surface and planted with turf and flowers. The rows of headstones would carry on the military idea, giving the appearance of a battalion on parade. The existence of individual headstones would go far to meet the wishes of relatives who above all things were in favour of the single grave. Also, the uniform headstones would convey the idea of equality though the pattern inscribed on them might vary. Each headstone would bear a regimental badge, the name, rank, regiment, and date of death of the victim and a short inscription supplied by the next of kin. The inscription would be subject to censorship since it was 'clearly undesirable to allow free scope for the effusions of the mortuary mason, the sentimental versifier, or the crank.' In practice, much doggerel was permitted and only the profane, the distasteful, and the impolitic were disallowed. The masons at Portland enjoyed carving

'He did his bit
And then got hit'

which perhaps gains in epitome what it lacks in lyricism.

Every cemetery, Kenyon continued, should have a monument to serve both as a shelter and as a chapel and should be adequately enclosed, the designs being simple and inexpensive. Isolated graves and small cemeteries should be concentrated into larger units in order to make the cemetery buildings economic. Horticultural experts and architects should co-operate over the designs which Kenyon himself would approve, and a register of those either buried or commemorated should be prepared for each cemetery. General simplicity of design with well-cut and well-proportioned lettering was regarded as essential, particularly as intricate carving would add greatly to the cost and would tend to become obliterated and lost in the course of time. A special committee was therefore set up consisting of MacColl of the

Wallis Collection, Sir Charles Holmes, of the National Gallery, and Macdonald Gill who, like his brother Eric, was an expert typographer.

In each cemetery there should be a Stone of Remembrance, and a Cross of Sacrifice, a tall finely proportioned stone cross with a symbolic sword of bronze attached to its face thus emphasizing both the military character of the cemetery and the religious affiliation of the majority of the dead. The Stone of Remembrance, which was Lutyens' idea, was to be 'a great fair stone of fine proportions 12 feet in length lying raised upon three steps and bearing in indelible lettering 'some fine thought or words of sacred dedication'.

Rudyard Kipling chose a quotation from Ecclesiastes for Lutyens' Stone of Remembrance—'Their name liveth for evermore'. The Cross of Sacrifice was to be designed by Reginald Blomfield, another eminent architect. With these guide-lines on which to work the Commission appointed three Principal Architects to design one cemetery each in order to test out Kenyon's ideas and to achieve a more accurate idea of the cost involved. The first three principal architects were Reginald Blomfield, Herbert Baker and Edwin Lutyens.

While these cemeteries were still on the drawing board, a battle ensued between the Commission and the British Treasury as to control of expenditure. It was not until June 1919 that Ware with Macready and three dominion representatives met Austen Chamberlain, Chancellor of the Exchequer, and Sir George Barstow of the Treasury; after much argument it was agreed that the British contribution to the cost of the Commission should be a grant-in-aid, and that although a Treasury official would attend meetings of the finance committee he would not exercise any control on behalf of the Treasury over the Commission's expenditure. The Commission then went on to set up agencies abroad, which resulted in a quicker start to its work and a considerable saving of money. Agencies were soon established in Egypt, Malta and Gibraltar, while the Dominion governments arranged for war graves within their own territories.

It would have seemed that the Commission now had all the powers it needed to go forward with a programme based on its three abiding principles: a headstone instead of a cross, the principle of uniformity, and the ban on repatriation. However there was a great public outcry against these principles, especially against the headstone; the main line of complaint being that if private initiative were allowed at home it was wrong to prevent it abroad. Although the Commission wanted to complete the experimental cemeteries before driving these differences to a common conclusion with the public, the opposition was not to be abated.

Parliament was divided, and Lord Belper led an anti-Commission lobby favouring a cross rather than a headstone for war graves. After much lobbying the report stage of the War Graves Commission estimates was reached; Winston Churchill had become the Commission's new Chairman. It remained for his eloquence to silence the opposition and the amendment to the Commission's principles was withdrawn. Churchill had said 'in periods as remote from our own as we ourselves are from the Tudors, the graveyards in France of this great war shall remain an abiding and supreme memorial to the efforts and the glory of the British Army. Even in two thousand years,' said Churchill 'Lutyen's Stones of Remembrance will preserve the memory of a common purpose pursued by a great nation in the remote past and will undoubtedly excite the wonder and reverence of future generations.'

The count at the end of the Great war amounted to 1,115,000 dead, made up of 584,000 identified graves and 530,000 men known to be dead and missing. There were 180,000 unidentified graves. The situation in France was appalling; most of the dead, both buried and unburied, lay along the line of the Western Front, which was a maze of ruined roads, railways, and bridges, crossed with trenches, covered with miles of rusting barbed wire, and impregnated with unexploded shells. The Commission took over its near-impossible task with great courage and met problems and setbacks which would have chilled the hearts of less courageous men. The first programme of the Commission set down in October 1919 included contracts for constructing 27 cemeteries in France and Belgium containing 49,000 graves. This initial crash programme was but a tithe of the total work to follow. A 'wholesale demobilization' in November 1919 of men working in the offices of the Directorate of Graves Registration and Enquiries in France cut off the supply of records and cemetery plans to the Commission at a time when the Commission's work was expanding at an amazing rate. In the year to March 1919 the Commission had spent only £7500, but 12 months later this figure had risen to a quarter of a million pounds. By the middle of 1920 work was proceeding on 788 cemeteries in France alone and even this was not fast enough: in the following January the Commission was warned that it might have to take over a further 1500 cemeteries within six months.

In the event, 'the experimental cemeteries' were all built by Blomfield and their cost averaged about two-and-a-half times the estimated costs which had been based on 1914 prices; the cemeteries finally chosen for this purpose were at Le Treport, Forceville and Louvencourt. The most successful was Forceville, where 'the cemetery, enclosed in breast-high walls crowned with flowers and backed with yew hedges, was a neat enclosure of shorn grass and white Portland Stone walks'. It was given a vertical proportion by some old poplars which had been left in place and new lindens which were planted to give shade. The experiment with these three cemeteries served its purpose however, for it became apparent that excessive decoration could be heavy and the feeling given by the cemetery at Forceville showed that treatment must depend on the individual site.

At this stage the Commission were considering materials and cost. Lutyens was unwilling to alter the design of his Stones of Remembrance which cost £500 each to make, carry and install. They weighed no less than eight tons each, and could look somewhat incongruous in tiny cemeteries. Lutyens' sole concession however was to allow the Stone to be built up in segments where a site made it difficult or impractical to erect it whole. Blomfield's Cross of Sacrifice was provided in three sizes ranging from 18 to 32 feet in height to suit the proportions of the cemeteries. Economies were made in the small cemeteries; here shelter buildings were eliminated, and Lutyens' Stone was omitted altogether, which infuriated him. Blomfield submitted designs for a standard building to be used in all the smaller cemeteries in France and Belgium thus saving the cost of separate designs for some 1500 structures. At one point increased costs seemed to make the Commission's total task unattainable, but in fact it was the size of the task which eventually solved the problem. Through increasingly favourable exchange rates and economies possible only because of the large scale of the enterprise, the early estimates were slashed by millions of pounds, and the simplicity and good taste of the Commission's work contributed to a lower rate of expenditure.

Half a million headstones all of the standard size, 99.06 × 38.1 × 7.62 cm, were required, and these were expected to cost £5 each including transport and erection; the difficulty was the cutting of the complicated regimental design and an individual inscription on each of them. Although the Monumental Masons Federation undertook to cope with the provision of the half million inscribed stones within six years they could not carve the badges, each of which took a skilled mason one week to cut. One of the Directorate's officers, Lieutenant Berrington, put forward a scheme for etching the badges in an acid process, but after testing, this was abandoned and the Commission stayed with hand carving. The Commission adhered to the principle of permanence and this over-rode the problems of cost, time, and shortage of skilled labour. Artificial stones, concrete stones, and badges cast in plaster were all considered and abandoned. Granite and marble were ruled out because of their basic cost and hardness. Finally the curator of the Geological Survey Museum recommended the commission to use Portland stone and stone from Hopton Wood in Derbyshire; these were both cheap, reliable, and British.

The 850 headstones for the three experimental cemeteries were produced at an average cost of only £3. 9s. which, though not including the cost of inscribing and engraving the badge, was an encouragement to the Commission who had expected a higher figure. The Commission recruited and trained into the masonry industry demobilized soldiers who went on to make most of the Commission's headstones. Through the inventiveness of a Lancashire firm a machine was devised on the principle of a pantograph which could cut the patterns of regimental badges and inscriptions onto the stone, enabling that company to make 50,000 stones in the first few years. The inclusive cost eventually came well below £5, and the 10 year period for producing all the headstones started to look like a possibility. Ten million cubic feet of good stone was to be quarried, carved, and delivered to sites spread over thousands of square miles. Behind all this physical work was the formation of a massive card index system to identify names, countries, and regiments alphabetically for the purpose of reference by individual relatives of the dead.

The Register of the Directorate of Graves Registration and Enquiries slowly collected particulars of name, rank, number, unit and regiment of the dead, with military honours and date of death in addition to age, parentage and other personal particulars. There followed a classified list of graves with ground plans, maps and photographs. A document was then prepared for each cemetery giving its position, accessibility, history, and the Commission's title to the land; this was added to the collated details of all the dead, and after editing, was sent to H.M. Stationery Office for printing. It was to take another 10 years to record and classify such information on over one million dead. When in 1922 King George V with Queen Mary made a pilgrimage to the war cemeteries, he said 'In the course of my pilgrimage I have many times asked myself whether there can be more potent advocates of peace upon earth than this multitude of silent witnesses to the desolation of war.'

By this time the Commission had hardly begun its work in the commemoration of the half-million dead who had no known grave. The majority of these dead lay beneath the soil of Passchendaele and the Somme. Inevitably there was divided opinion as to how the soldiers names should be commemorated and Kenyon presented three possibilities: one was individual headstones worded in such a way that obviously no bodies lay beneath them; or the names could be inscribed on cemetery walls; or a monument such as a cenotaph bearing the names could be erected in each cemetery. Many many arguments were put forward for and against each alternative, but the solution came from an unexpected quarter.

Late in 1919 Winston Churchill had obtained Cabinet agreement that Britain should pay for general memorials to the army as a whole, to be erected on the principal battlefields, that is at Ypres, Mons, Arras, the Hindenburg line, and on the Somme; at Gallipoli and in Jerusalem. As a result the National Battlefield Memorials Committee was appointed under the chairmanship of the Earl of Midleton, and the members included the Dominion

High Commissioners. During the inevitable discussions and disagreements that followed, one fact emerged. Unless something were done to stop it, two sets of memorials would be erected at unnecessary cost to the government,—memorials to the national effort on the battlefields and memorials to the missing soldiers. Sensibly the Secretary of State for War proposed to the Cabinet that the War Graves Commission should also take over responsibility for National Battlefield memorials. Rapidly a plan was developed for building 12 major monuments spread along the battle line from Nieuport on the Belgian coast to Soissons in the south and the names of the missing dead would be engraved in panels on these memorials.

Blomfield was commissioned to design the Menin Gate, and Kenyon's proposal that the other Principal Architects, Lutyens, Baker and Charles Holden should each be given the opportunity of creating a major memorial was approved by the Commission, the rest being thrown open to public competition. At Ypres, Blomfield was advised by local architects that the subsoil there was a solid layer of clay, but the careful Blomfield had one or two trial holes dug and discovered to his horror running sand. As a result the Menin Gate was built on a raft of concrete which rested on huge reinforced concrete piles thrust 36 feet into the sand. Blomfield's concept of the Menin Gate echoed the great Roman triumphal arches that he admired so much (see Plate 45). First was a huge vaulted hall approached through a monumental archway. Broad flights of stairs rose at each side towards a rampart which gave out at either end to four pavilions. The main arch was surmounted by a massive lion 'not fierce and truculent but patient and enduring—a symbol of the latent strength and heroism of our race.' It was arranged that the names of the dead should eventually be engraved on stone panels which could be fixed after the building had been finished. All the panels were to be of Portland stone. In all there would be 1200 of these panels in 30 different sizes ranging along the main hall, stairways, and loggias of the memorial.

The Menin Gate could not contain the names of all those reported missing in the Ypres salient and it was necessary for some names to be inscribed in Tyne Cot Cemetery, at Passchendaele (see Plate 45). When the time came for the main panels to be fixed in the Menin Gate memorial, 54,896 names had been engraved and in all that detail the masons had made less than a 100 errors, mainly minor spelling mistakes. The Menin Gate was unveiled by the King of the Belgians in July 1927; the Commission had then been in existence for just over 10 years. It became the most famous of the war memorials in the battlefield, though the memorials designed by the other principal architects were superb. At Thiepval, Lutyens had created an abstract design of tremendous power (see Plate 46) and at Neuve-Chapelle Baker endowed his monument with a sense of peace and intimacy as well as a peculiarly Indian feeling which was appropriate to the part played in that theatre by Indian forces in the Great War.

By 1927 more than 500 cemeteries on the Western Front were complete, well over 400,000 headstones had been erected, 63 miles of hedges had been planted, and 540 acres sown with grass. A thousand of Blomfield's Crosses were erected and 400 of Lutyens' Stones emplaced all over the world. Portland stone had been used exclusively. The names of 150,000 missing servicemen had been inscribed on memorials; it was a year of great publicity for the Commission. There were inauguration ceremonies at the Menin Gate, Neuve-Chapelle, Nieuport, Soissons and La Ferté. The memorials to the missing at Le Touret, Vis-en-Artois, Pozierese and Cambrai were all dedicated on the same day of August in 1930, but it was Whit Monday of 1932 before the Prince of Wales inaugurated Lutyens' massive memorial at Thiepval and by then the task of completing all the cemeteries was at last achieved by the Commission. Rudyard Kipling described this as 'the biggest single bit of work since any of the Pharoahs, and they only worked in their own country'.

In these early days the Principal Architects had created a 'school of cemetery design' which derived from the need to limit cost, and one which reflected an association with the homely sense of the English churchyard'. In spite of standardization however each cemetery acquired some character of its own and in some cases reflected the humour of the British 'Tommy': thus three cemeteries were named Dozinghem, Bandaghem, and Mendinghem, names invented to commemorate original field dressing stations which stood on those sites. Another, Dud Corner had been built over an early mining area and suffered damage from subsidence.

Blomfield advised his junior architects to follow the straightforward methods of the formal garden with careful observance of the relative value of the expanses of grass in relation to the serried ranks of the white Portland headstones.

In April 1927 a Permanent Maintenance Scheme had been launched under which 134 gardener-caretakers were employed, and by 1930 the Permanent Maintenance Branch accounted for 567 of the 714 employees in France and Belgium. But maintenance cost money; the Commission had since 1921 pressed for the setting up of an endowment fund in accordance with the original Charter. In the long financial battle from 1921 right up to the outbreak of World War II the Treasury stood grudgingly between the Commission and its need for finance. The Treasury had expressed the intention 'to take advantage of any diminution of public interest in the graves as the years progressed until they might ultimately be allowed to disappear'. This shocked the Commission who pressed for a permanent endowment fund provided by the Empire governments. Although opposed by Winston Churchill, who was then Chancellor, the Canadian Prime Minister, Mackenzie King, gave active support together with the Australian Prime Minister, Stanley Bruce. The Baldwin Cabinet of March 1925, finally assured Britain's contribution to the capital sum required by the Commission, a sum sufficient to yield an income equal to the Commission's annual minimum expenditure estimated at £216,000. Although committed to the principle, the Treasury battled on undeterred to minimize its capital contributions; the Commission suffered not only in this way, for as the British Government contributions were made in government stocks, the Commission suffered when interest rates were reduced, and again in 1931 when Britain came off the gold standard.

Time was necessary to test the early cemeteries both in respect of the survival of horticultural decoration and the weathering of stone (see Plate 47). In Palestine, for instance, clouds of locusts could suddenly appear and leave plants and trees stripped behind them. When the cemeteries were irrigated, however, plants such as eucalyptus, oleanders and palms, roses, tamarisks and Persian lilacs grew readily in most of the cemeteries of Mesopotamia. The four main dangers to stone were storm, flood, earthquake, and particularly salt-laden soil. Storms could be strong enough to break up stonework, and the attrition of sandstorms obliterated inscriptions in North Africa. Flooding necessitated the bodily removal of a cemetery at Lake Nyasa to higher ground. A cemetery at Jerusalem was damaged by earthquake in 1928, and another in 1937 badly cracked the chapel at Gaza. However, soils with high salt and chemical content produced the most damage, not only making horticulture impossible, but eroding the stone rapidly. The particular areas of damage were in Iraq, Egypt, and Portuguese East Africa. A number of remedies were tried out: where water was available the ground could be irrigated and crops of lucerne raised to stem the damage, but where water was scarce other materials had to be tested. These included protective bitumen in Persia, and silico-fluoride in Egypt. The Commission received valuable help from the National Physical Laboratory and the Geological Surveys Museum.

A method of protecting the foot of headstones by placing them on concrete foundations coated with pluvex was tested, and another method was to re-position the headstones on long concrete beams standing six inches above the ground. It was finally decided that only granite or slate would serve in Egypt and that the stone from the quarries of Hopton Wood in Derbyshire though satisfactory for Palestine and Persia, was useless there. Portland stone stood up perfectly in northern Europe but from the latitude of Gibraltar and south, was better replaced by Cornish granite. It was often found that the advantages of a good local stone would outweigh the general preference for British stone. With present day technology, Portland stone can be used with impunity anywhere in the world, but the Commission concluded that its employment of Portland stone in the Middle East and North Africa had then been a misuse: replacements were made in indigenous stones, and eventually in marbles from Botticino in Northern Italy. Throughout the battle grounds of Europe, Portland stone has weathered perfectly and maintenance has cost far less than on other stones in the Middle East and North African zones.

The Menin Gate produced one big problem for the Commission; not because of the quality of the name panels which were all of Portland stone, but because of the original design whereby many thousands of names engraved in letters five-eighths of an inch in depth were placed too high for visitors to be able to read them from ground level. At a cost of £7000 the Commission in the late 20's had brought in an army of signwriters to paint the engraved letters black, using three coats of paint for the purpose. But the ravages of time and the Second World War eventually rendered these engravings illegible once more. In 1974 the Commission invited tenders for repeating the painting operation, only to find that at current costs of labour and materials, £70,000 would be required, which the Commission could not afford. The Director of Works of the Commission and his staff then formed their own 'think tank' and came up with a remarkable solution.

The panels of the Menin Gate were first hung with wallpaper lining; next, the surface was exposed to a flame gun which burnt the surface of the paper only where there was oxygen behind it, hence burning away only the paper over the lettering. Then came an air gun to blow out the burnt fragments of paper, and finally came a team of painters with spray guns who successively sprayed three coats of paint onto the masked surface. It then remained only to wash away the paper from the surface: the job was done for precisely £7000—the same as had been paid nearly 50 years earlier (see Plate 47). This work was undertaken because of continuous complaints of relatives—proving the sustained interest in the memorial, 50 years after the signing of the Armistice in 1918.

Fabian Ware continued his crusade for international understanding through the work of the Commission in the years between the wars. He even succeeded in bring about an Anglo-German-French agreement on war graves which was signed in Berlin on 20th November, 1935. The Germans fell into line with other countries in exempting the Commission from customs duty and agreeing that the graves in each country should not be disturbed. A Mixed Committee consisting of six British, six German and two French members was set up, but the workings of this committee became increasingly tense: France was a distrustful partner, for her relations with Germany were fast deteriorating. When addressing the National Conference of the Volksbund Deutsche Kriegsgräberfursorge in Cologne in that year Ware said 'armed conflict between our great nations would result in deeper wounds, wounds so deep that they would defy healing'. He was applauded not for the sentiment he was trying to express, but for the fact that it suited admirably the growing lust of the German leaders for revenge: at that time the Germans saw no purpose in the healing of wounds. Even up to May 1939 Ware managed to conduct the affairs of the Mixed Committee with some cordiality, and an informal agreement was reached under which Great Britain and Germany assured the care of enemy graves in the event of war; that was virtually the last useful act of the Mixed Committee.

On the outbreak of war, Ware returned to the War Office as Director of Graves Registration and Enquiries but still remained in charge of the Commission, thus co-ordinating the work of both authorities. With the wealth of experience behind Ware, an efficient relationship in the field was quickly established between the Commission, the Directorate, the British Expeditionary Force and the French authorities; and in the strange atmosphere of the 'phoney war' up to May 1940, work in the cemeteries of France was continued by the gardeners very much in the peacetime manner. The story of the 10th May offensive that took the Germans to Dunkirk is well known, and the breaking up of the Commission's organization in France was typical of the reigning chaos behind the lines. Following two weeks in which instructions were either not received or being received were impossible to achieve or ignored, the evacuation of the battle zones 'happened by itself'.

It was only possible to pick up the threads of the organization again as it reached non-combatant territory. Of the 540 Commission employees in France and Belgium 334 reached England, a surprisingly large proportion. The first to arrive on the 22nd of May telephoned the Commission, by that time housed at Wooburn Green in Buckinghamshire: their news was 'very coldly received'. The British seemed to be totally unaware of the position in France and Belgium. All the returning staff were absorbed into a labour-hungry war industry; a register was made of those willing to return to the continent when possible, and 19 out of every 20 names were on it.

In September 1940 when the bombing of Britain started in earnest, Ware wrote to Winston Churchill stating that the deliberate slaughter of civilians by the enemy was creating a new category of war casualties which he felt the Commission should not omit to commemorate. Churchill had no objection and thought that 'the number of civilian dead might well exceed the service dead in the Second World War'—a forecast in which he was wrong. As a result of Ware's move a series of leather bound volumes were prepared listing the civilian dead of the War, and six copies of the final printed version were handed over to the Dean of Westminster by the Duke of Gloucester in 1956.

The Second World War called for many new cemeteries and the Commission wanted 'the same general architectural and horticultural treatment to be accorded to cemeteries of the present war as to the last'. The aged Kenyon chose Hubert Worthington, who had served in the Great War, to control architectural policy; Worthington had assisted Lutyens and held the Chair of Architecture at the Royal College of Art. Worthington insisted on cemeteries containing at least 2000 graves in order to establish economic units for maintenance, and he did everything to preserve military associations. 'Names like El Alamein, Halfaya, Sollum, Tobruk, Acroma and Mareth had to be perpetuated', he said. As the war was coming to an end public interest in war memorials was renewed and the Commission reiterated its policy of banning the repatriation of war graves from overseas. Ware became a member of a group set up to advise the Adjutant-General on the subject of campaign and unit monuments, and a Battle Exploits Memorial Committee was again set up, as it had been after the Great War. The time had come for the government to ensure proper co-ordination between the Commission, the Battle Exploits Memorial Committee and the Dominions; in the end unity was achieved, all the participatory countries and their agencies agreeing to band together in commemorating the missing.

By the end of 1945, 245 members of the Commission's staff were already back on the Continent, and a further 110 were waiting impatiently to follow them. The task before them was enormous. In the Second World War there were a further 347,056 graves to be marked with headstones, and 233,012 missing dead were to be commemorated. The Commission now had to care for 24,000 sites all over the world. And, in a world of shortages, the Commission had to face another round of hardships and arguments, though fortunately it had ended the war in a strong financial position with over six million pounds in the endowment fund, and with accumulated reserves of £550,000. However the expenditure on the Great War graves alone had now risen to £347,000 a year—50% above the annual product of the fund in interest. The suggestion was made that a separate endowment fund should be set up for graves of the Second World War, but in the current political climate there was no point in pursuing the matter, and the Commission gave up hope of ever being self-supporting.

By 1947 Fabian Ware had reached the age of 77 and the strain of a lifetime's battle in the interests of the Commission had 'sapped his energies and impaired his judgement, if not his tenacity'. In November of that year Higginson succeeded Ware, who stayed on as Vice-Chairman. But in June 1948 Ware finally retired, and died in the following April in his 80th year. Fabian had been twice knighted, receiving the KBE in 1920, and KCVO in 1922. On his death the great commemorator was in turn commemorated by a plaque in the Warrior's Chapel at Westminster.

Without Ware the role of the Commission seemed to change. No longer was it a political force, but rather 'a tried and venerable institution'. Public opinion was changing too: Empire was dissolving into Commonwealth; in 1950 India pressed for 'Imperial' to be dropped from the Commission's title, but it took 10 years before the title 'Commonwealth War Graves Commission' was adopted. The main principles of the Commission had been established under Fabian Ware: Higginson concentrated on administrative reform, and the vexed question of finance. No longer was there a feud with the Treasury, only the problem of how to achieve broad objectives with insufficient money. The Forces wisely fell in with the prevalent mood. The Admiralty and Merchant Navy agreed to extensions of their Great War memorials at Tower Hill and at the manning ports, though three new memorials at Lowestoft, Lee-on-Solent, and Liverpool were raised for the Royal Naval Patrol Service, the Fleet Air Arm, and Merchant Seamen serving with the Royal Navy. A new memorial for the Air Force was raised at Runnymede, while the Army and Air Force shared memorials at El Alamein and Singapore.

Plans for cemeteries and war graves had been going forward. Starting with the taking over in 1946 of the old cemeteries in

France and Belgium, the commission turned next to Normandy, and through branch offices first at Arras and then at Brussels, rapidly took under its care all British war graves round the world. By the late '40's the Commission was ready to begin construction, and turned again to Portland as the chief supplier of stone; the supply was sufficiently rapid to warrant the opening of a special factory by Griggs and Son at Sugar House Lane, Stratford in east London, where a number of headstones were engraved. For each regimental badge the Commission had to buy a template with machinery costing £1500. Production of headstones at Portland rose to 600 per week, many of them being engraved at Bottomcombe and shipped abroad, a number as far as Australia. By the early '50's production at Portland was at its height, a rate of about 1000 headstones per week, and by 1956 90% of all new graves were permanently marked. In addition to headstones, the quarries and masonry at Portland were called on to add Stones of Remembrance and Crosses of Sacrifice to their production, a truly formidable task that was accomplished with patient efficiency (see Plate 47).

Far behind the drive to complete the war graves programme came plans in 1948 for the construction of new cemeteries. Sir Hubert Worthington, Louis de Soisson, Philip Hepworth and Sir Edward Maufe became Principal Architects, and survived what seemed interminable delays and insuperable difficulties in producing memorials and cemeteries which reflected not only the principles set down by the Commission but the ethos of the countries in which they were built. The inauguration of the major memorials were great occasions, many ceremonies being performed by royalty. The first Cross of Sacrifice to be inaugurated after the War, at Great Bircham, was unveiled by King George VI in 1946. The Naval Memorial at Chatham was unveiled by Prince Philip in 1952; the Air Force Memorial at Runnymede by the Queen in 1953; and the memorial at Bayeux by the Duke of Gloucester, the Commission's President, in 1955. In 1958 most members of the Royal Family assembled to dedicate the new memorial at Brookwood. Lord Montgomery unveiled the memorial at El Alamein, and Field-Marshal Alexander the memorial below the ruined monastery at Cassino.

As the major programme resulting from World War II came to fruition, the Commission reverted to the unending tasks of research and maintenance to keep its records right and its standards regular in a changing world; also there were new theatres of war and other international disputes which brought about new situations and changing policies for the Commission to administer. There would never be a time when no headstones were needed. At the time of Higginson's retirement in 1956, the call for headstones still averaged about 1000 a year. The Commission had reduced specifications to a standard for each kind of stone used, and an order for 1000 headstones in Portland stone, given to Saunders of Ipswich in 1958, specified that the stone should be cut on the natural bed, 'free from obvious imperfections in the structure of the stone such as vents, sand pockets, or creeches and shell occurring in such layers and in such positions as may seriously affect the strength of the finished headstone'. An angle-chamfered arris not exceeding one-sixteenth of an inch on either face should be taken off all edges of the stone which was to be 'smooth-rubbed' on all surfaces. The use of stopping of any kind was expressly forbidden. Lettering and figuring were to be cut true to a standard alphabet drawing, with a V-incision at the angle of 60°. Regimental badges were to be cut in flat silhouette carving without any modelling, to a depth of three-sixteenths of an inch.

By this time the Commission and its masonry contractors had purchased about 120,000 tons of quarried blocks of Portland stone, which represents some 100,000 tons of stone in finished work. In round figures—for accurate ones do not exist—40,000 tons had been used for headstones and 60,000 tons for Crosses of Sacrifice, Stones of Remembrance, and panels engraved for the missing dead. Around the world, but mostly in France and Belgium, there are now between seven and eight hundred thousand headstones of Portland stone.

19

---·❧·---

War Stories, 1939–1945

THE BRITISH PEOPLE, with a promise of 'peace in our time' still ringing in their ears, had watched the annexing of Austria, the overrunning of the Sudetenland and the threat to the Polish Corridor with an incredible measure of indifference. On the morning of Sunday 3rd September 1939, they were totally unprepared for war. The government had been led by Germany's numerous infractions of the Treaty of Versailles to embark on a rearmament programme in 1935; but consistently it turned a blind eye to the acts of expansionism which would only end in war. Finally the British and French governments gave Germany an ultimatum by guaranteeing Poland from attack. But Germany could afford to ignore the guarantee and face the consequences.

When the sober facts of war and the extent of Britain's involvement were made plain to the British, a process of strategic planning and tactical cunning evolved which used every resource, physical and mental, that the country could muster; this indeed was their genius. The integration of civilian with Forces effort was unparalleled in history: every commercial and industrial organization had a part to play. The size of that part would depend on the size of the organization and the measure and individuality of its skills. It often depended also on inventive genius, or the ability to see a novel wartime use for equipment performing mundane peacetime functions.

The Bath and Portland Stone Firms, as they were known in 1939, may have seemed an unlikely organization for war produc-

Processing stone at Bottomcombe: (above) a grinding machine puts in a groove, and (below) drilling dowel-holes for fixing.

Bottomcombe: (above) twin-bladed secondary saw, and (below) jointing
off after planing.

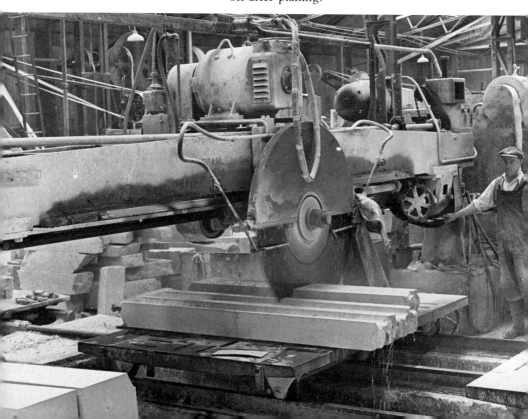

(a)

West Wells Masonry works: (a) turning a baluster, (b) and (c) banker masons 'finish' work that cannot be mechanized, routing into corners and stoolings, and removing 'boasted' stone.

(b)

(c)

(Above) Broadcasting House, for which architects G. Val Myer and Watson-Hart chose Portland stone.
(Below) Cunard House, in Leadenhall Street, another building of 1929–30, built in Portland stone.

(Above) Menin Gate designed by Reginald Blomfield for the War Graves Commission and unveiled by the King of the Belgians in 1927.
(Below) Tyne Cot Cemetery at Passchendaele, one of five hundred cemeteries completed on the Western Front by 1927.

(Above) Panels with names of the missing dead at Thiepval.
(Below) The memorial at Thiepval was designed by Sir Edwin Lutyens; Lutyens, Blomfield, and Herbert Baker were the three original Principal Architects appointed by the War Graves Commission.

(Above) Masons at Portland punching and tooling the shaft of a Cross of Remembrance.
(Below left) The War Graves Commission have an endless task of maintenance in War Cemeteries round the world.
(Below right) The experimental slab of stone used to devise an economic method of painting-in the names of the missing dead on the Menin Gate.

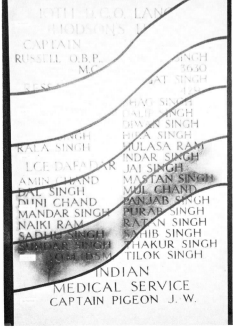

Opencast coal operations west of Barnsley during the Second World War. To reclaim 350,000 tons of good quality coal, the Company shifted nearly 4,000,000 tons of overburden.

tion. Their skills were in quarrying and fashioning stone, and the building and stone industries were rapidly made aware that their trades were ranked without priority except for work under government licence. Alan N. Pictor, then managing director of the company, was a man of vision who could see further than some of his contemporaries. By definition, The Bath and Portland Stone Firms were cutters and lifters of stone, a tough and heavy material. In their century-long fight to win stone from the ground, they had mined through 100 miles of underground galleries, at an average level of some 90 feet below the surface. These mines, Pictor had argued, must be far safer for storage of munitions, valuables, and emergency stores than surface premises strengthened against air attack. Furthermore they could be transformed into safe offices for essential personnel.

Business was tailing off rapidly in the masonry trade during 1938 and 1939 and Pictor was already negotiating for the taking over of a number of galleries in the hills to the east of Bath for storage of war materials. The conversion of the mines for administrative purposes was a specialized task and some of the Company's quarrymen and sub-contracting masons were put in for the preliminary work of making-ready horizontal and vertical surfaces out of rugged areas abandoned in earlier mining projects. It was during the preparation and occupation of these mines that an Admiralty official told Pictor that the Navy was experiencing difficulty in getting quartz cut in quantity.

It was the Anti-Submarine Detection Investigation Committee who urgently needed the quartz. Quartz is the hardest of stones and ranks number seven on Mohs' scale of hardness; it will scratch steel and glass, and is one of several crystals which when subjected to mechanical strain in particular directions will develop electrical charges. The Curies in Paris discovered this effect, known as the piezo-electric effect, in 1880. Subsequently a piezo-electric quartz plate was evolved for use both as a transmitter and receiver of high frequency sound, or ultra sonic waves. In contrast with low-frequency sound waves, which radiate in all directions, these high frequency waves in certain circumstances concentrate into a small angle creating a 'beam' effect, similar to the very short-wave radio beams used in radar.

Pierre Curie's successor as Director of the Paris École de

Physique et de Chimie worked on the application of high frequency piezo-electric oscillations to the location of submarines in the First World War. It would be unfitting to belittle either the success or the danger of submarines in the First World War, but the scale of activity at sea in the Second World War was huge by contrast, both in terms of merchant convoys and the number and range of submarines, especially the U-boats of Germany. The country desperately needed an instrument for transmitting a short-wave beam which could be fixed below water-level to every naval and merchant vessel in the Allied Fleets. Thus quartz in vast quantities had to be cut and to be cut quickly. It was in these circumstances that the Navy expressed its need to Alan Pictor. Only one firm, Childs of Yeovil, was engaged in this work and the method used was slow and costly. The cutting wheel made by Childs was an eight inch diameter steel disc to which diamond dust had been hammered on the outer edge.

At this time, H. Walter Pangbourne, manager of the Bottom-combe masonry works at Portland, had been engaged on experimental work with various types of disc saws for the cutting of Portland stone. Pictor had met Peter Neven, a chemist of Russian origin, in Antwerp in 1937, and had seen impregnated diamond wheels cutting tungsten carbide, stone, and other hard materials. Neven was working with the South African Oppenheimer diamond syndicate, and was the inventor of a process for the sintering of metal with diamonds. Very small particles of diamonds were mixed with a bronze or steel amalgam and fused together to form a hard segment which was brazed onto the periphery of a saw blade. Pictor arranged for Pangbourne to have a specimen cutting wheel made by Neven's process. Aware that Pangbourne had made good progress with this sintered disc, Pictor at once asked the Admiralty for a supply of quartz for experiments, and was soon able to invite officers to inspect the results.

The Admiralty were much impressed, but expressed doubt that with the heavy equipment available at Portland it would be possible to work to the very fine limits required. The machines on which the demonstration had been made were old and very big, whereas the tolerance required by the Admiralty was $+/-0.002$-inches in the width and thickness of the quartz sections. It was paramount that the finished product conform to these limits. By process of trial and error the masonry machinery at Portland was adapted: an 8 inch impregnated diamond blade was fitted to bearings and spindle held in special 'flappers' which were cast in the works; the flappers were then fixed to the cross-travel head of a planing machine in place of a normal tool holder.

Soon the Admiralty were convinced that the masonry works could satisfy their requirements and gave the order to proceed. The only new machinery purchased was a grinding machine from Anderson-Grice (Scotland) for the finishing process. No sooner had work started at Bottomcombe however, than the Germans started to bomb Portland as a military target. As the masonry works were on the Bill most bombs dropped into the sea, but this was not good enough for the Admiralty who ordered the immediate transfer of the quartz cutting operation. The Admiralty made an inspection of all The Bath and Portland Stone Firm's units and decided that the work should be split between the company's masonry works at Gloucester and the quarry site on the top of Ham Hill outside Yeovil. At Ham Hill, management was under Pangbourne and at Gloucester under A. T. Sharpe who had joined the company two years earlier. Pictor had brought Sharpe in to take charge of the Gloucester masonry works which had been opened for the supply of dressed stonework for the building of Newport Civic Centre.

The Admiralty had another concern for the security of the quartz cutting operation, however, in that Peter Neven and his little factory in Antwerp were the sole suppliers of sintered cutting wheels; Alan Pictor was sent hot-foot to Antwerp to ensure the continued supply of these diamond tools. The Admiralty called for the removal of the laboratory and its personnel to England as soon as possible, but Antwerp fell to the invading German army sooner than was expected, in February 1940. The equipment in Neven's laboratory was therefore seized by the Navy at the 11th hour; all the laboratory equipment down to the last screw, including presses, materials, and stocks was removed within a matter of 24 hours.

Peter Neven came to England, and with him came Grunburg, internationally famous as a diamond expert; Neffs, a diamond crusher and grader; Madame Vanoff, a mould-filler and mixer;

Jack Perney, engineer and lathe-turner; and Gregory (George) Fefer, in charge of sinter product-development and the pressing and firing of the steel blades. Neven was able to bring his family, but Fefer was hustled out of the country by air during the blackout; he left his wife and family in Belgium never to see any of them again, or to know what fate befell them. Nor did he have any idea where he landed in England. The machinery from Portland was divided and set up in the new works at Gloucester (the old workshop of the Manu-Marble factory), and Ham Hill. At Gloucester blocks of stone were moved around daily to confuse outsiders and make believe that stone was still being worked there for the building trade. The factory high up in the quarries of Ham Hill was so remote that no such diversion was necessary.

At the same time the shadow sintering factory was set up at Leeds. For the supply of diamonds for tool-making the Company had to apply to the Diamond Die and Tool Control. The Control operated from the sanatorium building of Rugby School under Controller, Sir Ronald Lindsay Prain, whose Senior Technical Officer, Len Burditt, dealt with industrial diamond tools. At Rugby, boart—an extremely tough, finely-crystalline form of diamond—was crushed, behind locked doors, and graded by falling through water. The Control gave financial assistance to die and tool manufacturers, and licensed the supply of dies and tools to registered users. The ubiquitous Pictor applied successfully for licences and help under the Capital Assistance programme, and after the war invited Burditt, an accountant, to join the Company.

The quartz cutting units at Gloucester and Ham worked for 21 hours in each 24 (three hours were needed for cooling, cleaning, and setting the equipment for the next day's programme). At Ham the whole complement lived on the Hill, sleeping, eating, and working there continuously, remote and unnoticed.

The method of cutting and assembly of the quartz was divided into three identifiable stages: the first was to take quartz in a variety of sizes supplied by the Admiralty and to reduce these to the correct thickness in cutting trays. The quartz was placed into these trays in sections fractionally over one-half inch in width, and as great in length as could be obtained from each piece of quartz. The pieces were then filled around with a liquid mixture which set hard when cold, thereby holding them rigid for cutting under the impregnated diamond blade. The trays were bolted to the bed of the planing machine which travelled in and out under the flapper. When the precise thickness of one-eighth-inch, within the prescribed tolerance of $+/-0.002$ inches, had been achieved, the trays were heated and the slabs released.

In the second stage, the quartz went to a testing room for establishing polarity, which in some cases could show both negative and positive on the same side of one piece. It was essential for the whole of one side of a finished unit to be of the same polarity. Thus sections of quartz having both negative and positive areas on the same side needed to be cut and re-assembled; a special machine for testing polarity was supplied and maintained by the Admiralty. Once the quartz was of the correct thickness and had where necessary been rectified for polarity, the strips were transferred to the grinding section, where they were finished to the precise width of one half inch, again to within limits of $+/-0.002$ inches. When the strips had been thus prepared they were cut to the greatest length possible: they were not cut square but to a parallelogram at a critical angle.

In this form the quartz passed to the third stage in an assembly room, where the pieces were fitted into a circular metal template or frame of approximately 12 inches diameter; this had metal strips running horizontally across it with a half-inch space between each metal strip. The sections of quartz were fed into these spaces, the outer edges being cut on a small grinding machine fitted with a six inch diamond grinding head, to shape the rows of quartz to the circumference of the frame. Approximately 12 rows of quartz sections completed one frame. When a template had been filled, the pieces were removed very carefully into a packing box which again was prepared with rows corresponding in number to the rows in the circular template. The boxes, each containing one complete assembly, were then delivered to the Admiralty, those at Gloucester being taken to a disused school in the town for hand-over.

In the finished equipment the circular quartz unit thus prepared was held between steel plates acting as electrodes which oscillated to generate the piezo-electric 'beam'. The instrument itself was in 1939 named ASDIC, an acronym of the initials of the Anti-

Submarine Detection Investigation Committee, but in 1963 the Admiralty announced that, to conform with NATO practice, the name ASDIC should be superseded by SONAR, an acronym of Sound Navigation (and) Ranging, which the United States had adopted in 1946. In the House of Commons, Winston Churchill later attributed the saving of much of the British Merchant Navy to the development and use of ASDIC.

While the Company's contribution to Operation ASDIC was developing, Pictor's discussions with the Ministry of Supply led on to Operation Tilefer, a contract which entailed the supplying and erecting of cranes over the country at various points between Aberdeen and Plymouth. There was an acute shortage of cranes in the country and the Company was in a good position to help, since the use of its equipment in quarrying operations had almost completely fallen away. John Lister-Kaye, who had been working for John Mowlems in Staffordshire, moved in 1942 to Kingswood at Bristol to erect gantries and a multiple span building for The Bath and Portland Stone Firms as a headquarters for repairing and distributing cranes of all types. Derrick cranes and overhead gantry cranes came mainly from the quarries at Portland, or from the masonry works there and near Bath. It took some three to four months for the Bristol depot to be completed and then Lister-Kaye travelled around the country re-erecting cranes at various locations and managing a repair service.

Operation Tilefer included the handling of crated American vehicles, prior to despatch to their assembly points. The Bath and Portland Stone Firms were able to provide a large number of their own cranes, including wooden hand derricks of which there were 12 at Whitchurch, each capable of lifting 10 tons. From the new depot, cranes of all descriptions were hired out by the Company in various directions, including one which it was told it could have if it would first take it down—from the top of the Protestant cathedral in Liverpool; which, of course, it did.

In the early 40's the Ministry of Agriculture made urgent requests to the company to produce ground limestone for agricultural purposes at their stone cutting works at West Wells. Equipment was put in, but because of the character of oolitic limestone, the plant failed very badly, and only achieved an output of one or two tons an hour using six or seven men in the process, until when the war was over, the machinery was modified by Lister-Kaye, and the output was doubled.

Another approach made by the government was a opencast coal production. When the cranage work had been completed early in 1944, Lister-Kaye was sent north to an opencast site three miles west of Barnsley (see Plate 48). This was a particularly arduous site with 100% rock of hard, gritty character. But the mechanical mind of Lister-Kaye was match for it. Here the sintered drill was used to produce a total of 350,000 tons of good quality coal; to reach the coal it was necessary to remove overburden to the extent of some three-and-three-quarter million cubic yards. This and work at two other opencast sites, one in east Yorkshire and one in Derbyshire, produced a total of nearly 900,000 tons of coal in the period 1944 to 1948. In the course of the Tilefer and opencast coal operations the Company had accumulated a vast range of equipment suitable for cutting, lifting and shifting minerals. It was to become the nucleus of a plant hire department.

The sintering of metal with diamonds meant more to George Fefer than cutting quartz. Fefer was born of Belgium parents at Tiflis in Georgia, and was brought at an early age from Russia to Brussels to be educated, finally graduating at the Sorbonne in Paris as an electrical engineer. He met Peter Neven at a diamond exhibition, and was invited to join Oppenheimers' laboratory in Antwerp; there he worked on various applications for industrial diamonds including sintering. Once Fefer was in England the applications of the sintered cutting wheel were put to early use. At the instigation of Alan Pictor, Portland went into the production of glass prisms for tank periscopes, and Pictor himself tested out the multiple cutting of block stone with these blades to produce slabs 2 inches in thickness. From these experiments came the principle of cladding buildings using stone that was independent of building stress and weight.

20

---·❧·---

The Platform of Opportunity

L OOKING BACK THROUGH the 57 years progress of The Bath
and Portland Stone Firms up to the end of World War II, the
names of four men stand out above all others. The founder
chairman, C. James Pictor, had set the Company on its feet and
laid down and implemented the twin policies of economy and
expansion by the time he retired in 1898. Five years later came T.
Sturge Cotterell as manager of the Company. The declining
profits recorded during his years of employment serve more as a
mirror of history than as a reflection of the work done by this
brilliant administrator. Inevitably, he was seconded to the Ministry of Munitions when war came: his loss to the Company was
immeasurable. The third man was Alfred Taylor, who had joined
the company at its inception as Chief Clerk; he was elevated to
company secretary in 1913, Director in 1914, manager in 1915
(when Sturge Cotterell retired), and managing director in 1920.
Taylor had a sixth sense for communications, and this empathy
found him time and again in the critical position which led on to
the company's expansion and success.

When Alan N. Pictor succeeded Taylor as managing director in
1932, the trust was passed on to him directly from one who had
served his founder-grandfather. Alan Pictor embodied most of the
abilities of Sturge Cotterell and Taylor combined, and added to
them an entrepreneurial skill that broadened the Company's base
as war came and went once more. Pictor was energetic and
ubiquitous; at once a perfectionist and a humanitarian, he drew
respect from quarryman, supplier and customer alike—while

getting his way with them. He had a mind for the order of things and the board of directors were now better informed than they had ever been before.

His appointment as managing director was well timed, for with his flair for opportunism, he could see the broad field of diversification shining clearly ahead. Pictor realized that over all the Company's history the directors had pressed onward but not outward, owning more and more quarries and masonries, and marketing more stone. He had seen the plight of the Company in the long periods when the building trade was slack, and he remembered the disastrous effect the first war had had on the company. As the clouds of war started to gather once more, he was determined that it should not be the Company's lot to repeat its earlier performance: being a monopolist in oolitic limestone was in itself no panacea, but it did mean that many skills had been mastered, and that experts were at hand to turn these skills to the advantage of the country. Sturge Cotterell had been on that track 25 years earlier. Alan Pictor did not wait for war to be declared: by 1936, he was discussing deep shelter under the Wiltshire hills for a number of government uses; he successfully developed a liaison with Whitehall through which one activity led to another. These activities brought the Company safely through a period when the demand for building stone had been almost non-existent.

When the war ended Pictor reviewed the situation. It was certain that stone would ever be needed, from the best quality used in sculpture, fine architecture, and the facings of important buildings, to the lower qualities needed as ashlar, paving, filler and aggregates. But would this be the moment of decision to break out of the immured world of architects, builders, and local government surveyors? Could the Company's latent assets used in wartime activities be put to civilian uses in peacetime?

The war had seen the Company building, excavating, tunnelling, lifting, roadmaking, converting mines into cool stores and habitable offices, shifting overburden, mining opencast coal, supplying crushed limestone as a soil conditioner, using industrial diamonds, cutting quartz and glass and then metals, and repairing, shifting, and hiring out heavy equipment, including cranes. Might this not point to a place in several new industries, notably public construction, building, building materials manufacture, agricul-

221

ture, chemicals, machine tool and instrument making, light engineering, and even refrigeration?

But diversification has its own enemies, especially dilution of energies and resources, and over-trading. What was now needed was professional management, and this the quarrymen directors could not provide (see Fig. 8 page 229). First came Ronald B. Ogden, who from 1956 acted as Deputy Chairman to Alan Pictor, and succeeded to the Chair on Pictor's death in 1960. The new office of Group General Manager was created in 1956 and filled by Kenneth Selby. Ogden, who remained Chairman until 1975, appointed Selby as Managing Director in 1960, and they, heading a team of their selection, were to convert what had always been a stone combine into the multi-lateral group we know today.

Out of the Rock . . . tells the story of the first 90 years of The Bath and Portland Group. Its subsequent history—after the Second World War—will be told in a further volume.

Appendices

Appendix 1

Memorandum that on the Eleventh day of June In the Year of our Lord one thousand seven hundred and Ninety one, I, Richd. Lano of the Isle of Portland In the County of Dorset, Quarryman, then came into the parish church of Portland, and did then and there according to an ancient custom time out of mind, freely give unto my friend Willm. Hansford of the same place and county aforesaid, Quarryman, the fifth part of one Quarter, or the twentieth part of a weir or rubble ground undivided Called or known by the name of Under Weeck, bounded with the lands of Edw. Pearce and others on the North, and the Clift on the West and the Sea on the West and South part thereof, this my fifth part of one Quarter of a weir or rubble ground. I, Richd. Lano do hereby freely give unto my friend, Willm. Hansford, freely to him to give or to sell to him or his heirs for ever according to the custom of the Isle and Manner of Portland and with the yearly and customely Rent to the Lord in Cheef of the said Manner and appurtenances thereto belonging, and this being my free Church Gift, in witness whereof I have hereunto set my hand and Seale the day and year first above written.

Witnesses
    Edward Pearce
    Robert Attwooll   RICHARD LANO

Fig. 1 A Deed by Church Gift, Portland, 1791

Fig. 3 Early engraving of quarrying at Portland, c. 1746

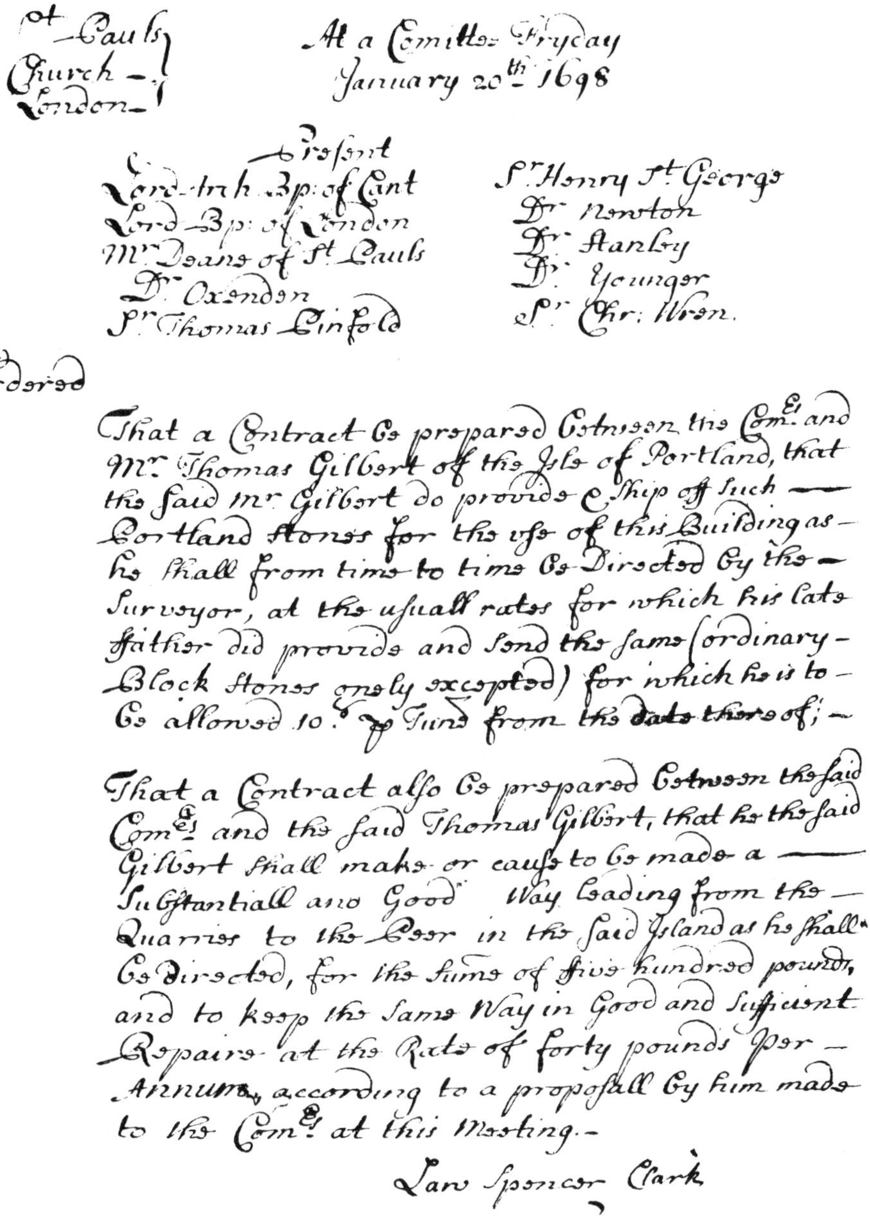

St Pauls
Church –
London –

At a Comittee Fryday
January 20th 1698

Present
Lord Arch Bp: of Cant
Lord Bp: of London
Mr Deane of St Pauls
Dr Oxenden
Sr Thomas Linfold

Sr Henry St George
Dr Newton
Dr Stanley
Dr Younger
Sr Chr: Wren.

Ordered

That a Contract Be prepared Betweene this Comee and
Mr Thomas Gilbert of the Isle of Portland, that
the said Mr Gilbert do provide & Ship of such
Portland Stones for the use of this Building as
he shall from time to time Be Directed by the
Surveyor, at the usuall rates for which his late
father did provide and Send the same (ordinary
Block Stones onely excepted) for which he is to
Be allowed 10s p Tunn from the date thereof; –

That a Contract also Be prepared Betweene the said
Comees and the said Thomas Gilbert, that he the said
Gilbert shall make or cause to be made a
Substantiall and Good Way leading from the
Quarries to the Peer in the said Island as he shall
Be Directed, for the sume of five hundred pounds,
and to keep the same Way in Good and Sufficient
Repaire at the Rate of forty pounds per
Annum, according to a proposall by him made
to the Comees at this Meeting. –

Law Spencer Clark

Fig. 2. Minute of St Paul's Cathedral affecting Sir Christopher Wren,
January 1698.

Memorandum That Thomas Gilbert of the Isle
of Portland in Dorsettshire doth Covenant with
the Rt Honorable the Lords and others Comrs for
rebuilding the Cathedrall Church of St Pauls London
that he the said Thomas Gilbert for the valuable
consideration of fifty pounds in hand paid, and the
further Sume of four hundred and fifty pounds to
be paid as is hereafter exprefsed to make sufficient
way for carriage of stone from the Kings Quarry
in the said Isle to the Crane and south peer adjoyning
the said way to be made with conveniency Stops—
for a sewers. Before for the nuff Cart, and other
for two Carts to meet without hazard, if foundation
to be firme upon ground that is not Logg and—
Slippery and more order to be made under the same
in proper places for Conveyance of the springs—
and Water. Covfes that in not weather and
from the Rock and all to be Rams and filld up
with Burs and Calkt and hard Rubbs of the
Quarry, all which is to be finished by the latter
end of August ensuing the date hereof and the said
Comrs Do agree that the said four hundred and
fifty pounds shall be paid proportionably as the—
work shall advanc and as Certificate of the same
shall be produced from Mr Dr Tucker of——

Weymouth and the like sume within sixty days——
after it shall be Certifyed as aforesaid by the said
Dr Tucker and by credible Workmen in ye Quarry
that the work is Compleat and perfect according
to the True Intention of these Articles. And
the said Thomas Gilbert doth further Covenant
with the said Comrs to preferve repaire and
maintaine the said way for the terme of
Seaventeen years to come from Michaelmas——
next for the yearly payment of fourty pounds,
the first payment to be made at Lady day then
next ensuing and so half yearly during the said
Terme, and to leave the way in good repaire—
after the expiration of the said Terme without
any further Demand (unavoidable accident may
happen) Except a generall stopp of the whole
ground such as happened in the year 1695

In Witnefs whereof the said Thomas Gilbert hath
hereunto Sett his hand and Seale this Six and Twentieth
Day of January Anno Domini 1698

This a True Coppy of the above mencond
Contract signed by Tho: Gilbert

Jac. Promer Clark
of the workes

The ELEVATION, to the North.

Of M.ʳ Allen's Houſe, in the Widcomb of Canalodunum, near Bath
with the Windows Dreſſed according to the Original Deſign.

Fig. 5 Prior Park detail.

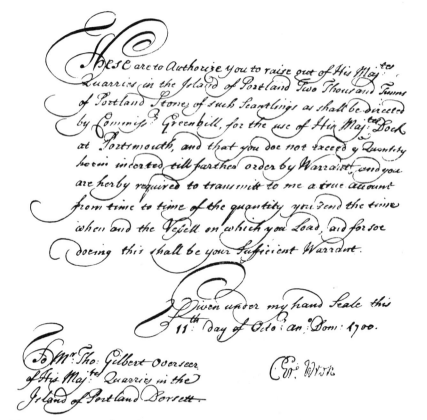

Fig. 6 A warrant from Wren to Gilbert, to raise 2,000 tons of stone for His Majesty's Dock at Portsmouth, October, 1700.

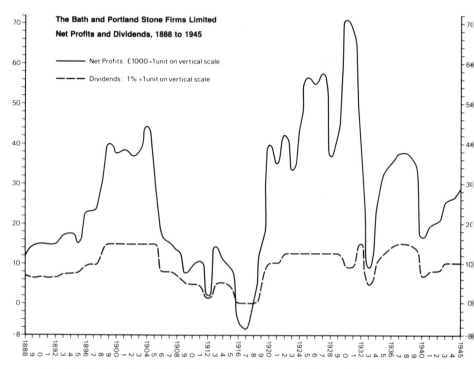

Fig. 7 The Bath and Portland Stone Firms Ltd: graph of profits and dividends, 1888–1945.

Year	Chairman	Managing Director	Directors	Manager	Secretary
1887	C. James Pictor (r. 1898)		Isaac Sumsion Snr. Richard Cripps (d. 1899) Robert E. Giles George Hancock (r. 1897) Herbert R. N. Pictor (r. 1907) Alfred W. Stone (r. 1889) James Stone (d. 1895) John T. F. Turner (d. 1912) James S. Randell (d. 1903) Isaac Sumsion Jnr.	George Hancock (r. 1897)	J. T. F. Turner (d. 1912)
1895					
1897					
1898	Isaac Sumsion Snr. (d. 1909)			William David (r. 1903)	
1903			Reginald D. Thornton		
1904				T. Sturge Cotterell (r. 1915)	
1907			Richard Lano (d. 1907) James McMurtrie (d. 1912)		
1909	Robert E. Giles (r. 1910)		Ald. James E. Henshaw JP, (d. 1918) Henry Sansom (r. 1919) Charles H. Long JP Alfred Taylor		Alfred Taylor
1910	Reginald D. Thornton (r. 1914)				
1912					
1913					
1914	Isaac Sumsion Jnr. (r. 1920)		Arthur C. Kinneir JP (d. 1928) Walter Pangbourne (d. 1938) Henry J. Sansom	Alfred Taylor	
1915					
1918					
1919					
1920	Charles H. Long JP (d. 1942)	Alfred Taylor (d. 1932)			H. Mallard (r. 1933)
1927			Walter F. Long Alan N. Pictor (Asst. M.D.)		
1928		Alan N. Pictor			
1932					
1933					R. N. Carter (r. 1958)
1938	Henry J. Sansom (d. 1944)		Walter J. Sansom (r. 1953) Gilbert G. Seymour (r. 1950) Stanley Long Amor (d. 1964) Ernest E. Way (r. 1953) Arwyn R. Davies Ronald B. Ogden		
1942					
1943					
1945	Walter F. Long (d. 1956)				
1950					
1953					
1956					
1957	Alan N. Pictor (r. 1960) Ronald B. Ogden (Dpty Chmn)		George Dickson OBE (d. 1963)	Kenneth Selby (Group Gen Manager)	
1958		Kenneth Selby			
1960	Ronald B. Ogden (r. 1975) Arwyn R. Davies (Dpty Chmn) (d. 1976)		Ronald F. Hill (r. 1967)		L. B. Burditt (r. 1971)

Fig. 8 The Bath and Portland Stone Firms management 1887–1960.

Appendix 2

A Short Bibliography

The Story of the Earth: Institute of Geological Sciences. H. M. Stationery Office. 1972

Continental Drift. D. H. and M. P. Harling. Penguin Books Ltd. 1975

Principles of Physical Geology. A. Holmes. Nelson. 1965

Prehistoric and Roman Wales. R. Mortimer Wheeler. Oxford University Press. 1925

Roman Bath Discovered. Barry Cunliffe. Routledge and Kegan Paul Ltd. 1971

The Island and Royal Manor of Portland. J. H. Bettey, MA. for the Court Leet in association with the University of Bristol. 1970

Wells Cathedral. R. D. Reid. Friends of Wells Cathedral. 1973

The Building of Bath. Bryan Little. Wm Collins & Sons Ltd. 1947

A Description of Bath, 1765. John Wood. Kingsmead Reprints. 1969

The Fashionable Stone. Kenneth Hudson. Adams and Dart. 1971

Bath Portrait. Bryan Little. The Burleigh Press. 1972

Georgian Summer. David Gadd. Moonraker Press. 1977

A Shortened History of England. G. M. Trevelyan. Penguin Books Ltd. 1972

Social History of England. G. M. Trevelyan. Penguin Books Ltd. 1974

The Evolution of Modern Industrial Organization. F. J. Wright. Macdonald and Evans Ltd. 1954

The Unending Vigil. Philip Longworth. Constable & Co Ltd. 1967

Index

Index

241